Essential

ITALIAN COOKERY

Essential ITALIAN COOKERY

CHANCELLOR
PRESS

First published in Great Britain in 1994 by Chancellor Press
an imprint of Reed Consumer Books Limited
Michelin House, 81 Fulham Road, London SW3 6RB
and Auckland, Melbourne, Singapore and Toronto

Designed and produced by SP Creative Design
Linden House, Kings Road, Bury St Edmunds, Suffolk, England
Editor and writer: Heather Thomas
Art Director: Al Rockall
Designer: Rolando Ugolini

ISBN 1 85152 662 5

A CIP catalogue record for this book is available from the British Library

Printed in Spain by Cayfosa, Barcelona.

Acknowledgements
Special photography: Graham Kirk
Step-by-step photography: GGS Photographics, Norwich
Food preparation: Maxine Clark and Dawn Stock
Food styling for cover photograph: Gillian MacLaurin
Styling: Helen Payne

Notes

1. Standard spoon measurements are used in all recipes.
1 tablespoon = one 15ml spoon
1 teaspoon = one 5ml spoon

2. Both imperial and metric measurements have been given in all recipes. Use one set of measurements only and not a mixture of both.

3. Eggs should be size 3 unless otherwise stated.

4. Milk should be full fat unless otherwise stated.

5. Fresh herbs should be used unless otherwise stated. If unavailable, use dried herbs as an alternative, but halve the quantities stated.

6. Ovens should be preheated to the specified temperature. If using a fan assisted oven, follow the manufacturer's instructions for adjusting the time and the temperature.

CONTENTS

1983
TALEGGIO
IGOR s.r.l.
NOVARA

INTRODUCTION

Italian cooking is incredibly diverse, and has evolved over many centuries. It derives from many classic European traditions: Roman, Byzantine and Greek. However, Italian food, as we know it today, stems from the Renaissance and the new discoveries and developments in the arts and sciences. Throughout northern and central Italy, in Florence, Venice, Milan and Rome, there was a new interest in food and a flowering of cookery skills as the great rulers experimented with new ingredients from the Far East and the New World.

The classic recipes from this exciting period of Italian history have been passed down through the generations and are now an established part of family and regional cooking. Every region has its own specialities, which are characterized by its climate, geography and local produce and fresh ingredients. Rome sits on the dividing line between the robust tomato and garlic flavoured peasant dishes of the Mediterranean south, and the more sophisticated and elegant dishes of the north.

Effectively, there is no real 'Italian' food, but there are classic Venetian, Roman, Sicilian, Bolognese and Neapolitan dishes, for example. From northern Italy come nourishing bean and vegetable soups, rustic stews, pasta in creamy sauces and delicate veal dishes, whereas from the south there are charcoal-grilled fish with vivid tomato sauces, caramelized oranges, sweet ricotta and mascarpone flans studded with crystallized fruit, and colourful stews of peppers, aubergines, tomatoes and olives which grow in the warm southern sun.

In Italy, good food and wine are a way of life, an intrinsic part of the Italian character and culture. Italians cook with the freshest ingredients of the highest quality: fine regional cheeses, local sausages, tender beef and veal, country hams, fresh fish and seafood, free-range chickens and numerous varieties of fresh pasta.

Family meals are rituals and consist of several courses. They start with antipasti – such as stuffed vegetables, prosciutto, salami or seafood salad – followed by *minestra,* (soup), and then pasta or a risotto, a fish or meat course with vegetables or salad, and then dessert and cheeses.

Anchovies

Packed in oil or salty brine, anchovies are a characteristic ingredient in many classic recipes from Piedmont and the south (Sicily and Calabria), especially bean dishes and stews. They are essential for making *bagna cauda,* a garlic and anchovy-flavoured dip from Piedmont, which is served with raw vegetable crudités

Arugola (rocket)

These dark green leaves have a distinctive peppery flavour and are often added to salads. They can be bought in many supermarkets, or you can grow them yourself.

Basil

This pungent, aromatic herb is used widely throughout Italy to flavour tomato sauces, salads, stews and casseroles. It is the essential ingredient in pesto, a sauce made from pounding garlic, pine nuts, olive oil, Parmesan cheese and fresh basil leaves, and which is served with gnocchi or fresh pasta. Fresh basil is always preferable to dried, and can be purchased in many supermarkets either in packets or growing in small pots all the year round.

Beans (fagioli)

Dried speckled borlotti beans or white cannellini beans are the beans most often used in soups and salads. They must be soaked in water overnight and then rinsed and drained before using. To cook them, bring to the boil in fresh water and then boil vigorously for a few minutes before reducing the heat to a simmer. Cook for about 1 hour, or until tender. Do not add salt to the cooking water as it will harden the beans.

Ceps (porcini)

These mushrooms are highly prized and quite expensive. Fresh ceps are hard to find but you can use the dried ones, which are available from most good Italian delicatessens and have a rich, concentrated flavour. Soak them first in warm water for 20-30 minutes.

Mozzarella

This fresh cheese is traditionally made from buffalo's milk and is sold packaged in its own whey. It should be dripping fresh with an elastic texture. It is the classic topping for pizza.

Olive oil

You can choose between fruity green oils, which make wonderful salad dressings, and lighter golden ones, which are used for frying and tossing pasta. Really, there is no substitute for olive oil in Italian cooking, and sunflower or vegetable oil are not suitable – they do not have the same flavour. In the north butter is used in many dishes instead of oil

It is worth investing in good olive oil, even if it is a little more expensive than the cheaper brands. Extra virgin oil, made from the first cold pressing of the olives, is best for dressing salads. Virgin olive oil is more suitable for cooked dishes and sauces.

Pancetta

This is raw pork belly which has been cured in salt and spices. It is usually used as a basis for stews and sauces, diced and then fried in olive oil with onion and garlic. If you cannot obtain pancetta, you can substitute ham or streaky bacon instead.

Parmesan

One of Italy's oldest and best-known cheeses, Parmesan is extremely hard and is aged over a long period, sometimes several years. It is sold split into rough lumps or ready-grated. To appreciate its strong flavour, it is best to buy it in pieces and then grate it freshly over pasta dishes.

Pasta

There are scores of different types of pasta, and every region has its own particular specialities and ways of serving them. You can make it yourself, or buy it freshly made of dried, coloured pink with tomato paste, green with spinach or even black with cuttlefish ink. Pasta is really only flour and water, sometimes enriched with an egg, but it is one of the most versatile Italian foods and may be baked, stuffed, tossed in sauces or vinaigrette dressing. It is found everywhere, all over Italy, in a variety of shapes and sizes (cylinders, spirals, shells, tubes, sheets and bows) and rejoices in wonderful evocative names – tortellini, ravioli, spaghetti, pappardelle, cappellacci, fettuccine and tagliatelle, to name but a few.

Pasta should be cooked uncovered in plenty of boiling water, to which a little oil and a generous pinch of salt have been added, until it is tender but still firm to the bite (*al dente*). Drain quickly and add a little butter or oil before using.

Pine nuts (pignoli)

These small creamy nuts are gathered from the cones of the stone or umbrella pine. They add texture and a distinctive aromatic flavour to many savoury dishes as well as cakes and biscuits. They are also an essential ingredient in pesto sauce.

Polenta

This yellow maize flour hails from northern Italy and is particularly popular in Lombardy and the Veneto region around Venice. It is boiled and then served steaming hot with stews, or it can be left to cool and solidify and may then be cut into slices and grilled, baked or fried in olive oil. Unfortunately, polenta is time consuming to cook and needs continuous stirring to get a smooth, lump-free finish. However, you can now buy quicker-cooking versions which take the hard work out of preparing polenta.

Prosciutto crudo

The best known of these cured raw hams are Parma and San Daniele, which are sold cut into wafer-thin slices. Prosciutto is salted and air-dried and usually has a faintly sweet flavour. It is often served as an antipasto dish with fresh figs or melon, or may be used in stuffings for veal and chicken.

Rice

The most commonly used rice is the short-grained Arborio variety. This has been grown in Lombardy for over 600 years and is an essential ingredient in risottos – the classic rice dishes of northern Italy. The grains swell to two or three times their original size and are plump and round. They have a moist, creamy consistency and are slightly firm when cooked. The secret of a good risotto is to cook it very slowly over low heat until all of the liquid has been absorbed and the rice is tender.

Salami

There are many regional varieties of salami, some of which are flavoured with peppercorns, garlic, herbs or chillies. They are usually made from ground pork and are flecked liberally with white fat. Salami is usually served thinly sliced, often with olives, as an antipasto dish, or may be added to stews and soups. Mortadella from Bologna is one of the largest and best known of these preserved sausages. The Napoli salami is hot and spicy, whereas the Milano is milder with a fine texture.

Tomatoes

These are essential to many Italian dishes, especially in the south. The Italian word for tomato is *pomodoro*, or 'golden apple'. Tomatoes are used fresh, canned, puréed, concentrated, sieved, sun-dried or preserved in fruity olive oil. Plum tomatoes are most commonly used for making sauces, which are flavoured with onion and garlic and served with pasta, vegetables, meat and fish dishes.

Equipment and utensils

Most Italian cooking utensils and kitchen gadgets are standard items in the western world, but there are a few specialist items that you might consider buying.

Coffee maker: you can buy genuine Italian machines for making expresso and cappucchino coffee. These range from the humble and inexpensive Moka-express and Neapolitan coffee maker to expensive steel and chrome hissing machines.

Pasta machine: this is very useful for making home-made pasta and reduces the time and labour of making it by hand. You can buy manual or electric machines but they are not worth the investment unless you adore pasta and plan to make it regularly.

Pasta wheel: this is a useful little gadget in wood or metal for cutting ravioli.

Pestle and mortar: in Italy, these are often made of marble. They are useful for making pesto sauce and pounding herbs and spices.

PASTA CON I FAGIOLI

White bean and noodle soup

1 Drain the beans and put in a large saucepan with the pork, onion, carrot, celery, garlic, parsley, sage, bay leaf and enough water to cover. Bring to the boil, then reduce the heat, cover the pan and simmer gently for 2 hours, or until the beans are soft.

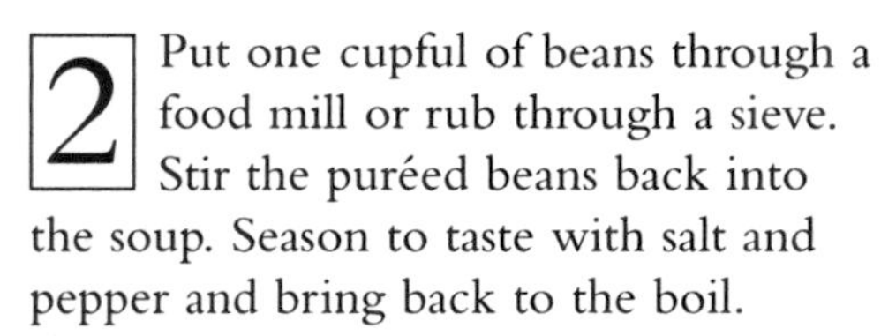

2 Put one cupful of beans through a food mill or rub through a sieve. Stir the puréed beans back into the soup. Season to taste with salt and pepper and bring back to the boil.

PREPARATION: SOAKING OVERNIGHT
COOKING: $2^{1}/_{2}$ HOURS
SERVES: 4-6

3 Add the spaghetti or noodles to the soup, and boil for about 12 minutes, or until the pasta is cooked and tender but still firm to the bite (*al dente*).

250g/8oz dried white beans, soaked overnight
250g/8oz pork belly with skin
1 onion, finely chopped
1 carrot, finely chopped
1 celery stick, finely chopped
1 garlic clove, crushed
3 parsley sprigs, finely chopped
1 sprig of sage, chopped
1 bay leaf
salt and freshly ground black pepper
175g/6oz spaghetti, ribbon noodles or vermicelli
2 tablespoons olive oil

4 Remove the pork from the soup. Cut off the rind and cut the meat into small pieces. Just before serving, drizzle the olive oil into the soup, and stir in the pork and a generous grinding of black pepper. Transfer to a tureen or individual serving dishes.

OLIO
di
POGGIOPIANO
OLIO EXTRAVERGIN
DI OLIVA

MINESTRONE

Italian vegetable soup

1 Place the haricot beans in a large bowl and cover with water. Leave to soak for 8 hours or overnight. Drain the beans and then rinse under running cold water.

2 Heat the oil in a large saucepan and add the onions, garlic and bacon. Sauté gently for about 5 minutes, stirring occasionally, until soft and golden brown.

3 Add the beans, water, herbs and tomatoes, cover the pan and simmer gently for 2 hours. Add the carrots and simmer for 10 minutes. Stir in the potatoes and turnip and cook for another 10 minutes.

- 125g/4oz haricot beans
- 3 tablespoons oil
- 2 onions, chopped
- 2 garlic cloves, crushed
- 2-3 rindless bacon rashers, chopped
- 1.75 litres/3 pints water
- 1 teaspoon chopped fresh marjoram
- ½ teaspoon chopped fresh thyme
- 4 tomatoes, skinned, seeded and chopped
- 2 carrots, diced
- 2 potatoes, diced
- 1 small turnip, diced
- 1-2 celery sticks
- 250g/8oz cabbage
- 50g/2oz small pasta shapes
- 1 tablespoon chopped fresh parsley
- salt and freshly ground black pepper
- 3 tablespoons grated Parmesan cheese + extra to serve

PREPARATION: 20 MINUTES + SOAKING OVERNIGHT
COOKING: 2½ HOURS
SERVES: 6

4 Chop the celery and shred the cabbage. Add to the soup with the pasta shapes and cook for 10 minutes, or until the pasta and all the vegetables are tender. Add the parsley and seasoning to taste. Stir in the Parmesan and then ladle into individual soup bowls. Serve immediately with extra Parmesan cheese.

INSALATA DI MARE

Seafood salad

1 Soak the mussels in a bowl of cold water and discard any that are open or rise to the surface. Scrub them well to remove any barnacles, and then remove the beards.

2 Put the mussels in a deep saucepan and add the water. Cover with a lid and steam over high heat, shaking the pan occasionally, until the mussels open. Steam for 2 more minutes and then drain and set aside to cool. Discard any that do not open and remove the others from their shells.

PREPARATION: 25 MINUTES
COOKING: 20 MINUTES
SERVES: 4-6

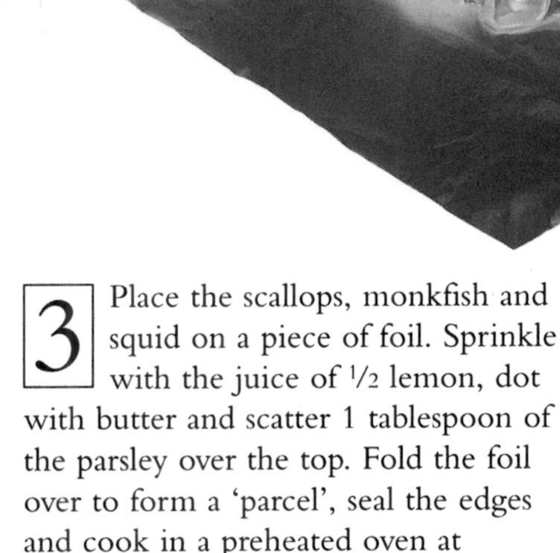

3 Place the scallops, monkfish and squid on a piece of foil. Sprinkle with the juice of 1/2 lemon, dot with butter and scatter 1 tablespoon of the parsley over the top. Fold the foil over to form a 'parcel', seal the edges and cook in a preheated oven at 190°C/375°F/Gas Mark 5 for 20 minutes, or until cooked.

- 600ml/1 pint mussels in their shells
- 125ml/4 fl oz water
- 8 scallops, cut into pieces
- 375g/12oz monkfish, cubed
- 125g/4oz squid, sliced
- juice of 2 lemons
- 15g/1/2oz butter
- 3 tablespoons finely chopped fresh parsley
- 12 king prawns
- 2 garlic cloves, crushed
- 4 tablespoons olive oil
- salt and freshly ground black pepper

4 Put the prawns in a baking dish and sprinkle with garlic, the juice of 1/2 lemon and 1 tablespoon of the chopped parsley. Bake uncovered for 10 minutes in the preheated oven. Arrange the cooked mussels, monkfish, scallops and prawns in a serving dish and sprinkle the remaining lemon juice and olive oil over the top. Season with salt and pepper, sprinkle with the rest of the parsley and refrigerate until required.

PEPERONI E MELANZANE RIPIENI

Stuffed peppers and aubergines

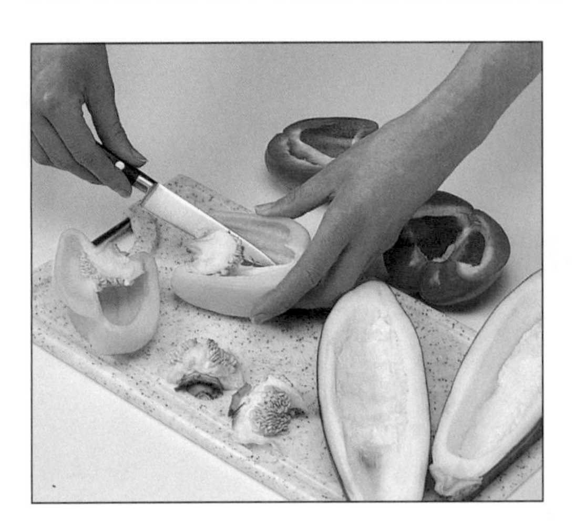

1 Cut the aubergines and peppers in half lengthways. Carefully scoop out the aubergine flesh, chop it roughly and sauté in 2 tablespoons of the olive oil until golden and soft. Remove the seeds and stalks from the peppers.

2 In a bowl, mix together the chopped tomatoes, anchovies, garlic, basil or marjoram and parsley. Add 50g/2oz of the grated cheese, pine nuts and breadcrumbs and the sautéed aubergine mixture. Season to taste with salt and pepper.

PREPARATION: 20 MINUTES
COOKING: 50 MINUTES
SERVES: 4

3 Lightly oil a large shallow ovenproof dish with a little of the olive oil. Fill the aubergine and pepper shells with the breadcrumb mixture, smoothing the surface of each one. Arrange them in the oiled ovenproof dish.

- 2 aubergines
- 1 large yellow pepper
- 1 large red pepper
- 7 tablespoons olive oil
- 500g/1lb large tomatoes, skinned and chopped
- 50g/2oz canned anchovy fillets, drained and chopped
- 2 garlic cloves, crushed
- 2 tablespoons chopped fresh basil or marjoram
- 2 tablespoons chopped fresh parsley
- 75g/3oz grated Pecorino or Parmesan cheese
- 2 tablespoons pine nuts
- 50g/2oz fresh white breadcrumbs
- salt and pepper

4 Sprinkle with the remaining grated cheese and dribble the rest of the olive oil over the top. Bake in a preheated oven at 200°C/400°F/Gas Mark 6 for 50 minutes or until golden-brown. You can serve the peppers and aubergines hot or cold. Either way, they are equally delicious.

FRITTATA

Vegetable omelette

- 3 tablespoons olive oil
- 2 onions, very thinly sliced
- 3 courgettes, thinly sliced
- 3 tomatoes, skinned and chopped
- 6 large eggs
- salt and freshly ground black pepper
- 50g/2oz grated Parmesan cheese
- few fresh basil leaves, chopped
- 1 tablespoon chopped fresh parsley
- 25g/1oz butter

To serve:

- grated Parmesan cheese

1 Heat the olive oil in a large frying pan. Add the sliced onions and sauté very gently for 8-10 minutes until really soft, golden brown and almost caramelized. Add the courgettes and continue cooking until golden on both sides, stirring from time to time. Add the tomatoes and cook over moderate heat until the mixture is thick.

2 Break the eggs into a large bowl and add the seasoning, grated Parmesan cheese, chopped basil and parsley. Beat well with a wire whisk until they are thoroughly blended.

3 Drain off and discard any excess oil from the cooked tomato mixture. Add the mixture to the beaten eggs and stir together gently until they are well mixed.

4 Heat the butter in a large clean frying pan until it is hot and sizzling. Pour in the egg mixture and reduce the heat to a bare simmer (as low as it will go). Cook very gently until the omelette is firm and set underneath. Place under a preheated hot grill for a few seconds to set and brown the top. Slide out on to a plate, and serve at room temperature cut into wedges and sprinkled with grated Parmesan cheese.

PREPARATION: 25 MINUTES
COOKING: 10 MINUTES
SERVES: 4

ANTIPASTO

Pepper salad and leeks in vinaigrette

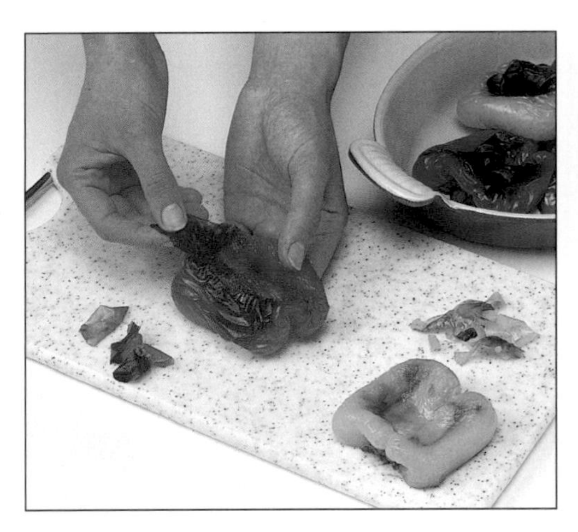

1 Place the peppers under a hot grill and cook them until they are black and blistered. Turn them occasionally to cook them evenly on all sides. Place in a polythene bag until they are cool, and then peel away the skins.

2 Cut the peppers open and remove the seeds. Cut the flesh into thin strips and arrange them in a serving dish. Sprinkle with olive oil and scatter with parsley and garlic. Finally, grind a little sea salt over the peppers.

3 Cook the leeks in a large saucepan of lightly salted boiling water for about 10 minutes, or until they are tender but still firm. Drain them thoroughly in a colander and then transfer the leeks to a serving dish.

For the pepper salad:

4 red, green and yellow peppers
4 tablespoons olive oil
1 tablespoon chopped fresh parsley
2 garlic cloves, crushed or chopped
freshly ground sea salt

For the leeks in vinaigrette:

500g/1lb thin leeks, washed and trimmed
6 tablespoons olive oil
1 tablespoon lemon juice
2 tablespoons balsamic or wine vinegar
2 garlic cloves, crushed
salt and freshly ground black pepper

4 Mix together the olive oil, lemon juice, vinegar, garlic and seasoning until well blended. Pour the dressing over the leeks and serve either warm or cold with the pepper salad and some fresh ciabatta or crusty bread.

PREPARATION: 30 MINUTES
COOKING: 10 MINUTES
SERVES: 4-6

COZZE GRATINATE

Grilled mussels

2.4 litres/4 pints mussels
200ml/7 fl oz white wine
½ red pepper, seeded, and chopped
2 garlic cloves, crushed
4 tablespoons finely chopped parsley
425g/14oz can tomatoes, drained and chopped
5 tablespoons fresh white breadcrumbs
2 tablespoons olive oil
salt and freshly ground black pepper
1 tablespoon grated Parmesan cheese

1 Put the mussels in a large bowl, cover with cold water and discard any that are open or cracked or rise to the top. Scrub them well under running cold water to remove any barnacles and the beards. Put the cleaned mussels in a large saucepan with the wine and bring to the boil, covered with a closely fitting lid.

2 Cook the mussels over medium heat for a few minutes, still covered, and shaking the pan occasionally until the mussels open. Discard any mussels that do not open. Remove the open mussels from the pan and take off and throw away the top half of each shell.

3 In a bowl, mix together the chopped pepper, garlic, parsley, chopped tomatoes and 4 tablespoons of the breadcrumbs. Stir in 1 tablespoon of the olive oil and then season to taste with a little salt and some freshly ground black pepper.

4 Add a little of this mixture to each of the mussels in their shells and place them in an ovenproof dish. Sprinkle with grated Parmesan and the remaining breadcrumbs and olive oil and bake in a preheated oven at 230°C/450°F/Gas Mark 8 for 10 minutes. Preheat the grill and flash the mussels under the hot grill for a crisp finish.

PREPARATION: 30 MINUTES
COOKING: 10 MINUTES
SERVES: 4-6

TAGLIATELLE AL SUGO DI POMODORO

Tagliatelle with tomato sauce

- 4 tablespoons olive oil
- 2 onions, chopped
- 2 garlic cloves, crushed
- 500g/1lb plum tomatoes, skinned and chopped
- 2 tablespoons tomato paste
- 1 teaspoon sugar
- 100ml/4 fl oz dry white wine
- a few ripe olives, stoned and quartered
- a handful of torn basil leaves
- salt and freshly ground black pepper
- 375g/12oz dried tagliatelle
- 50g/2oz grated Parmesan cheese

1 Heat 3 tablespoons of the olive oil in a large frying pan. Add the onions and garlic, and sauté gently over low heat until they are tender and slightly coloured. Stir the mixture occasionally.

2 Add the tomatoes and tomato paste together with the sugar and wine, stirring well. Cook over gentle heat until the mixture is quite thick and reduced. Stir in the quartered olives and torn basil leaves and season to taste with salt and plenty of freshly ground black pepper.

3 Meanwhile, add the tagliatelle to a large pan of boiling salted water (to which a little oil has been added to prevent the pasta sticking). Boil rapidly until the tagliatelle is tender but still firm (*al dente*, or 'firm to the bite').

4 Drain the tagliatelle immediately, mixing in the remaining olive oil and a generous grinding of black pepper. Arrange the pasta on 4 serving plates and top with the tomato sauce, mixing it into the tagliatelle. Serve sprinkled with Parmesan cheese.

PREPARATION: 10 MINUTES
COOKING: 20 MINUTES
SERVES: 4

PASTA ASCIUTTA

Fresh home-made pasta

300g/10oz strong plain bread flour, sifted
pinch of salt
3 eggs
1 tablespoon olive oil
flour for dusting

To serve:
olive oil
finely chopped garlic
salt and freshly ground black pepper
finely chopped fresh parsley

1 Put the flour and salt on a work surface. Make a well in the centre and add the eggs. Using your fingertips, draw the flour in from the sides and mix well. Add the olive oil and continue mixing until you have a soft dough. Alternatively, you can make the dough in a food processor.

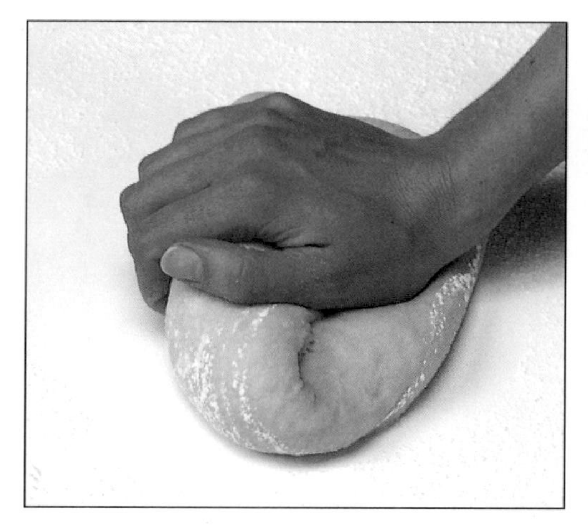

2 Turn the dough out on to a lightly floured surface and knead well until it is really smooth and silky. Roll out the dough, giving it an occasional quarter-turn and stretching it out, until it resembles a thin sheet of cloth and is almost transparent.

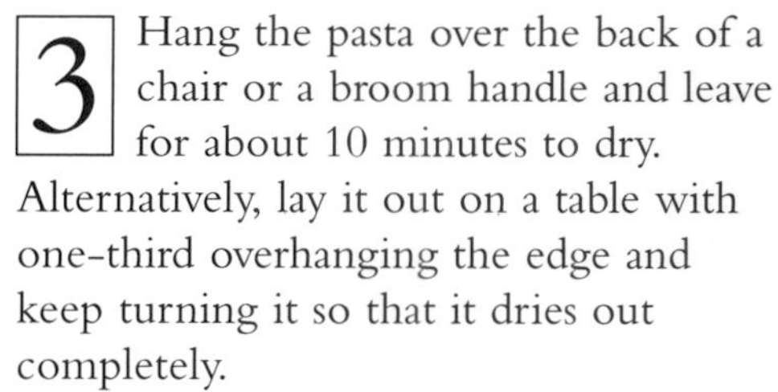

3 Hang the pasta over the back of a chair or a broom handle and leave for about 10 minutes to dry. Alternatively, lay it out on a table with one-third overhanging the edge and keep turning it so that it dries out completely.

4 Roll the pasta up loosely like a Swiss roll and then cut through horizontally at regular intervals to make fettuccine(3mm/$^1/_8$ inch wide) or tagliatelle (5mm/$^1/_4$ inch wide).

Unravel them and toss gently in a little flour. Leave them to dry on a cloth for at least 30 minutes before cooking in salted boiling water. Serve with a sauce or simply tossed with olive oil, garlic, salt and pepper and parsley.

PREPARATION: 1 HOUR
COOKING: 2-3 MINUTES
SERVES: 4

Note: To make lasagne or ravioli, cut into sheets rather than strips.

CANNELLONI

Baked stuffed pasta rolls

8 pieces wide lasagne
1 tablespoon vegetable oil
25g/1oz grated Parmesan cheese
15g/½oz butter
For the filling:
2 tablespoons olive oil
50g/2oz chopped onion
1 garlic clove, crushed
250g/8oz finely minced beef
2 tomatoes, skinned, seeded and chopped
1 tablespoon fine breadcrumbs
25g/1oz grated Parmesan cheese
¼ teaspoon dried marjoram
1 egg, lightly beaten
salt and freshly ground black pepper
For the sauce:
40g/1½oz butter
40g/1½oz flour
300ml/½ pint hot milk
150ml/¼ pint hot single cream
salt and pepper
grated nutmeg

1 Make the filling: heat the oil in a saucepan, add the onion and garlic and sauté for 5 minutes until soft. Add the minced beef and cook, stirring, until browned. Add the tomatoes, cover and cook for 10 minutes over low heat. Remove the pan from the heat and stir in the breadcrumbs, cheese, marjoram, egg and seasoning. Set aside to cool.

2 Make the sauce: melt the butter in a saucepan and stir in the flour. Cook gently over low heat for 1 minute, stirring well. Remove from the heat and whisk in the milk and cream. Return to the heat and bring to the boil, whisking all the time, until thick and smooth. Season with salt, pepper and nutmeg to taste. Cover and keep warm.

3 Cook the lasagne with the oil in a large saucepan of salted boiling water for a few minutes, until tender but *al dente*. Remove the cooked lasagne sheets with a slotted spoon and drain well.

4 Spoon a little of the filling down one long side of each sheet of lasagne. Roll each one up into a cylinder. Arrange the cylinders side by side in a well-buttered ovenproof dish. Spoon the sauce over the top to cover the pasta completely. Sprinkle with Parmesan cheese, dot with butter and then bake in a preheated oven at 190°C/375°F/Gas Mark 5 for 20-30 minutes until bubbling and golden.

PREPARATION: 30 MINUTES
COOKING: 20-30 MINUTES
SERVES: 4

SPAGHETTI ALLA CARBONARA

Spaghetti with bacon and egg sauce

1 Bring a pan of salted water to the boil, adding a little oil if wished to prevent the spaghetti sticking together. When the water reaches a rolling boil, add the spaghetti to the pan and continue boiling until it is cooked through but still firm to the bite *(al dente)*. Drain well.

2 While the spaghetti is cooking, chop the bacon rashers into small pieces and sauté in the olive oil in a large saucepan until cooked and golden brown.

PREPARATION: 5 MINUTES
COOKING: 15-20 MINUTES
SERVES: 4

3 Add the drained cooked spaghetti to the pan and gently stir in the beaten eggs, salt and freshly ground black pepper and cream. Stir very gently over a low heat until the egg starts to set.

4 Toss the spaghetti mixture lightly with most of the Parmesan cheese and serve immediately while still very hot, sprinkled with the remaining Parmesan cheese and the chopped parsley.

500g/1lb spaghetti
8 rashers streaky bacon
2 tablespoons olive oil
3 eggs, beaten
salt and freshly ground black pepper
3 tablespoons single cream
50g/2oz grated Parmesan cheese
2 tablespoons chopped fresh parsley

TAGLIATELLE AL PESTO

Pasta with basil sauce

1 Spread the pine nuts out on a baking sheet and place in a preheated oven at 220°C/425°F/Gas Mark 7 for 3-5 minutes, until golden. Keep checking them to make sure that they do not burn.

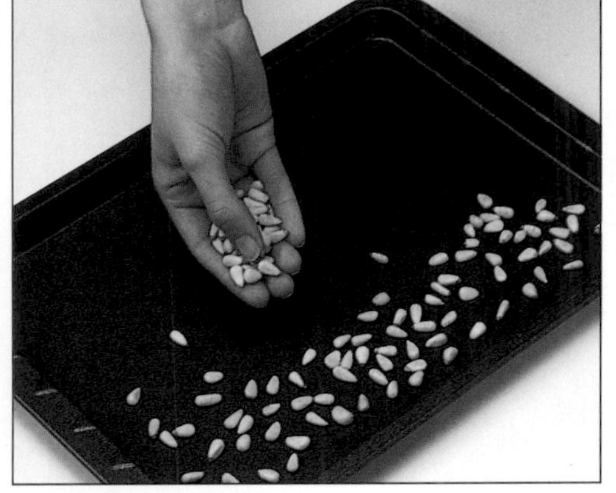

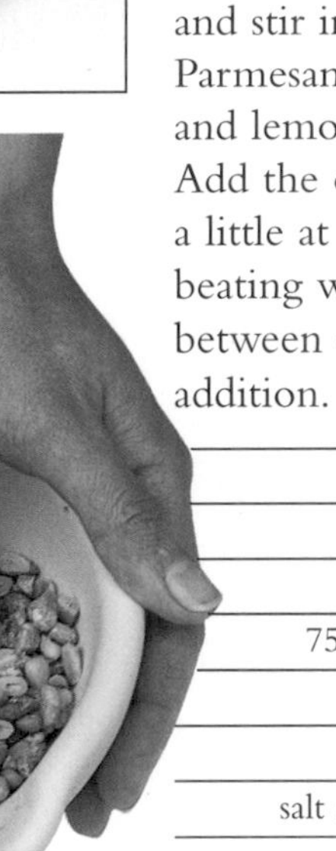

2 Put the pine nuts with the garlic in a mortar and pound the mixture to a thick paste. Alternatively, you can use a blender or food processor for this.

3 Tear the basil leaves into shreds and add to the pine nut mixture in the mortar, blender or food processor. Continue pounding or processing until you have a thick green paste. Transfer to a bowl (if using a mortar) and stir in the Parmesan cheese and lemon juice. Add the olive oil, a little at a time, beating well in between each addition.

- 50g/2oz pine nuts
- 1 garlic clove, crushed
- 50g/2oz fresh basil leaves
- 75g/3oz grated Parmesan cheese
- juice of ½ lemon
- 125ml/4 fl oz olive oil
- salt and freshly ground black pepper
- 500g/1lb tagliatelle

To serve:

- 50g/2oz grated Parmesan cheese

4 Bring a pan of salted water to the boil and add the tagliatelle. Cook until just tender and *al dente* (literally 'to the bite') and drain well. Sprinkle with freshly ground black pepper and toss the pasta lightly with the pesto sauce. Serve sprinkled with Parmesan cheese.

PREPARATION: 15-20 MINUTES
COOKING: 5-12 MINUTES
SERVES: 4

LINGUINE ALLA MARINARA

Linguine with mussels and tomato sauce

3 Add the shelled mussels and mix gently into the tomato sauce. Simmer the mixture over low heat for 2-3 minutes, or until the mussels are heated through.

1 Prepare the mussels: cover them with cold water and discard any that open or float to the surface. Scrub the remaining mussels and remove the beards. Place in a large saucepan with 100ml/4 fl oz water, cover with a lid and cook over moderate heat until the mussels open, shaking the pan occasionally. Drain the mussels and remove the shells, leaving a few in their shells for decoration.

2.25 litres/4 pints mussels
3 tablespoons olive oil
1 onion, chopped
3 garlic cloves, crushed
750g/1½lb tomatoes, skinned and chopped
salt and freshly ground black pepper
500g/1lb linguine
3 tablespoons chopped parsley

PREPARATION: 25 MINUTES
COOKING: 20 MINUTES
SERVES: 4

2 Heat the olive oil in a frying pan and add the onion and garlic. Sauté over medium heat until golden and tender. Add the chopped tomatoes and seasoning, and cook gently over low heat until the mixture is thickened and reduced.

4 Meanwhile, cook the linguine in salted boiling water until tender (*al dente*). Drain well and gently toss with the tomato and mussel sauce. Transfer to a serving dish or 4 warm plates, sprinkle with chopped parsley and garnish with the reserved mussels.

BOTTLED AT THE SOURCE, S. PELLEG
S.PELLEG
CARBONATED NATURAL
750 ml

RAVIOLI DI SPINACI E RICOTTA

Spinach and ricotta ravioli

one quantity home-made pasta dough (see page 26)
For the filling:
250g/8oz spinach leaves
125g/4oz fresh ricotta cheese
25g/1oz grated Parmesan cheese
salt and freshly ground black pepper
grated nutmeg
1 egg, beaten
To serve:
50g/2oz butter, melted
3-4 fresh sage leaves, torn
grated Parmesan cheese

1 Make the filling: wash the spinach leaves and remove the stalks. Put the spinach in a saucepan without any water, cover with a lid and cook over very low heat for 5 minutes. Drain the spinach in a colander and press down firmly with a plate to squeeze out any excess moisture. Roughly chop the drained spinach.

2 Put the ricotta and Parmesan cheeses in a bowl and mix in the chopped spinach. Add the seasoning, grated nutmeg and beaten egg, mixing well to a paste.

3 Roll out the pasta as thinly as possible on a lightly floured surface and cut into 2 equal-sized pieces. Put teaspoons of the ricotta and spinach filling over one piece of pasta at intervals, about 5cm/2 inches apart.

4 Cover with the other sheet of pasta and press gently around each little mound with your fingers. Using a pastry cutter wheel, cut the pasta into squares. Cook the ravioli in gently boiling water for 4-5 minutes, until they rise to the surface. Drain and serve with melted butter, sprinkled with sage and Parmesan cheese.

PREPARATION: 25 MINUTES
COOKING: 4-5 MINUTES
SERVES: 4-6

Barco Reale
1991
VINO DA TAVOLA
DI TOSCANA
750 ml

SPAGHETTI ALLA BOLOGNESE

Spaghetti with meat sauce

1 Make the sauce: heat the oil in a saucepan or deep frying pan and sauté the onion, garlic, bacon, carrot and celery until soft and golden. Add the beef and cook, stirring occasionally, until browned.

3 Add the milk and a little grated nutmeg and stir well. Continue cooking until the milk has been absorbed by the meat mixture. Add the tomatoes, sugar and oregano. Reduce the heat to a bare simmer and cook, uncovered, for 2-2½ hours until the sauce is reduced and richly coloured.

2 Add the red wine and bring to the boil. Reduce the heat slightly and cook over medium heat until most of the wine has evaporated. Season with salt and freshly ground black pepper.

PREPARATION: 10 MINUTES
COOKING: 2½-3 HOURS
SERVES: 4

500g/1lb spaghetti
1 teaspoon olive oil
freshly ground black pepper
50g/2oz grated Parmesan cheese

For the bolognese sauce:
4 tablespoons olive oil
1 onion, finely chopped
1 garlic clove, crushed
4 rashers streaky bacon, rind removed and chopped
1 carrot, diced
1 celery stick, diced
500g/1lb minced lean beef
150ml/¼ pint red wine
salt and freshly ground black pepper
125ml/4 fl oz milk
grated nutmeg
425g/14oz canned chopped tomatoes
1 tablespoon sugar
1 teaspoon chopped fresh oregano

4 Bring a large saucepan of salted water to the boil. Add the spaghetti and olive oil and cook until tender but *al dente* (firm to the bite). Drain well and season with freshly ground black pepper. Serve with the bolognese sauce, sprinkled with Parmesan cheese.

LASAGNE AL FORNO

Baked layered pasta

1 Make the ragu sauce as per the instructions on page 110. Simmer gently for at least 1 hour until it is time to assemble the lasagne.

2 Make the white sauce: melt the butter in a saucepan and stir in the flour. Cook over gentle heat, without browning, for 2-3 minutes, and then gradually beat in the milk until you have a thick, smooth, glossy sauce. Season with salt, pepper and nutmeg, and cook gently for 5-10 minutes.

PREPARATION: 1¼ HOURS
COOKING: 30 MINUTES
SERVES: 4

3 If you are using dried lasagne, drop it into boiling salted water and cook until just tender. Drain and pat dry. Put a little of the ragu sauce in a buttered ovenproof dish and cover with a layer of lasagne and then another layer of ragu topped with some white sauce. Continue layering up the sauce in this way ending with a layer of lasagne and a topping of white sauce.

250g/8oz dried lasagne sheets or freshly made lasagne
1 quantity ragu sauce (see page 110)
50g/2oz grated Parmesan cheese
15g/½oz butter
For the white sauce:
40g/1½oz butter
40g/1½oz flour
600ml/1 pint milk
salt and freshly ground black pepper
pinch of ground nutmeg

4 Sprinkle with grated Parmesan cheese and then dot the top with butter. Bake in a preheated oven at 230°C/450°F/Gas Mark 8 for 30 minutes until the lasagne is golden brown. Serve hot with a green salad.

RISOTTO CON PORCINI

Mushroom risotto

1 Heat half of the butter in a large heavy frying pan, add the onion and fry gently until it is soft and translucent. Take care that it does not become too coloured.

2 Add the sliced mushrooms and cook for 2-3 minutes, stirring occasionally. Add the rice and stir over a moderately low heat until all the grains are glistening and beginning to turn translucent around the edges.

3 Stir in a ladleful of boiling stock and simmer very gently until it has been absorbed. Continue adding more stock in this manner until the rice is thoroughly cooked and tender and all the liquid has been absorbed. This will take about 15-20 minutes. Halfway through cooking, stir in the saffron. Stir frequently to prevent the rice sticking to the base of the pan, and season with salt and pepper.

125g/4oz butter
1 onion, finely chopped
375g/12oz mushrooms, thinly sliced
500g/1lb risotto rice, e.g. Arborio
1.2 litres/2 pints boiling stock
1/8 teaspoon powdered saffron or saffron threads
salt and freshly ground black pepper
40g/1 1/2 oz grated Parmesan cheese

To serve:
2 tablespoons chopped parsley
freshly grated Parmesan cheese

4 When the rice is ready, gently mix in the remaining butter and the Parmesan cheese. The risotto should not be too dry – in fact, it should be quite moist. Serve the risotto sprinkled with parsley and some more grated Parmesan cheese.

PREPARATION: 5 MINUTES
COOKING: 30 MINUTES
SERVES: 4

RISOTTO ALLA MARINARA

Seafood risotto

1 Scrub the mussels thoroughly under running cold water and discard any that are cracked. Place in a large saucepan with a little water, and boil, covered, until they open. Shake the pan occasionally. Strain and set aside, retaining the cooking liquid.

2 Heat the olive oil in a large deep frying pan. Add the onion and garlic and fry gently until they are soft and golden, stirring from time to time.

3 Stir in the rice and cook over low heat for 1-2 minutes, stirring until the grains are glistening with oil and almost translucent. Pour in some of the fish stock and the reserved mussel liquid and wine, and bring to the boil.

600ml/1 pint fresh mussels in their shells
4 tablespoons olive oil
1 onion, chopped
2 garlic cloves, crushed
375g/12oz Arborio risotto rice
1.8 litres/3 pints fish stock
125ml/4 fl oz dry white wine
few strands of saffron
375g/12oz peeled cooked prawns
250g/8oz scallops
250g/8oz prepared squid
salt and freshly ground black pepper
2 tablespoons chopped fresh parsley

To garnish:

sprigs of fresh oregano

PREPARATION: 25 MINUTES
COOKING: 45 MINUTES
SERVES: 4-6

4 Meanwhile, soak the saffron in a little boiling water and add to the risotto with the prepared prawns, scallops and squid. Reduce the heat to a simmer and cook gently, adding more fish stock as necessary, until the rice is tender and creamy and all the liquid has been absorbed. Stir in the mussels and season with salt and pepper. Sprinkle with parsley and serve garnished with oregano.

SUPPLI ALLA ROMANA

Stuffed rice croquettes

1 Bring 600ml/1 pint water to the boil in a large pan. Stir in the gravy, tomatoes and butter, and pour in the rice. Mix well and simmer over low heat for 15 minutes, or until the rice is tender. Stir occasionally to prevent it sticking and add more water if necessary.

2 Meanwhile, sauté the ham and onion in the butter. Add the veal and cook until lightly browned. Add the tomatoes and simmer until reduced. Add the chicken livers and cook quickly. Season.

3 Remove the rice mixture from the heat, and stir in the grated cheese and beaten eggs. Season with salt and pepper. Turn the rice mixture out into a bowl and set aside to cool.

4 Put a rounded tablespoon of rice in the palm of one hand. Make a depression in the centre and fill with some of the meat mixture and 2 cubes of Mozzarella. Cover the filling with the rice and shape into a ball. Repeat with the rest of the mixture and coat the rice balls with breadcrumbs. Deep fry in hot oil, a few at a time, until golden brown. Drain on absorbent paper and serve hot.

PREPARATION: 20 MINUTES
COOKING: 45 MINUTES
SERVES: 4-6

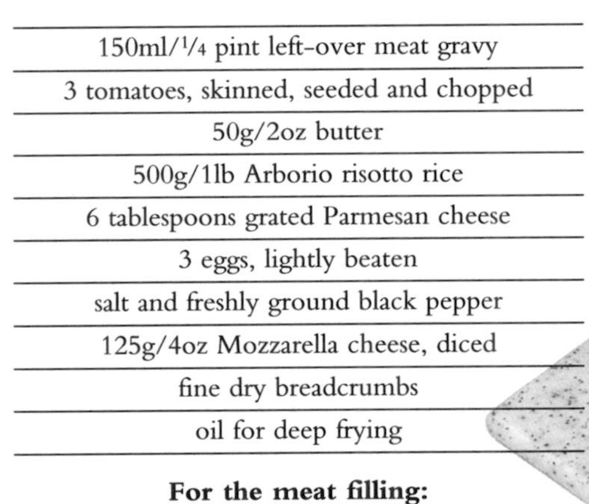

150ml/¼ pint left-over meat gravy
3 tomatoes, skinned, seeded and chopped
50g/2oz butter
500g/1lb Arborio risotto rice
6 tablespoons grated Parmesan cheese
3 eggs, lightly beaten
salt and freshly ground black pepper
125g/4oz Mozzarella cheese, diced
fine dry breadcrumbs
oil for deep frying

For the meat filling:

2 slices Parma ham (prosciutto crudo), shredded
1 small onion, finely chopped
50g/2oz butter
125g/4oz chopped veal
2 tomatoes, skinned, seeded and chopped
125g/4oz chopped chicken livers
salt and pepper

PIZZA NAPOLETANA

Neapolitan-style pizza

15g/½oz fresh yeast
2 tablespoons warm water
250g/8oz strong plain flour
1 teaspoon salt
2 tablespoons olive oil
3 tablespoons milk

For the topping:

4 tablespoons olive oil
1 x 425g/14oz can chopped tomatoes, drained
salt and freshly ground black pepper
1 tablespoon chopped fresh basil
1 teaspoon dried oregano
175g/6oz Mozzarella cheese, sliced
4 tablespoons grated Parmesan cheese

1 Blend the yeast with the warm water in a small bowl. Leave in a warm place for 10 minutes until frothy. Sift the flour and salt into a large bowl, make a well in the centre and pour in the yeast mixture, oil and milk. Gradually draw the flour into the liquid and mix to form a stiff but pliable dough, adding more milk if necessary.

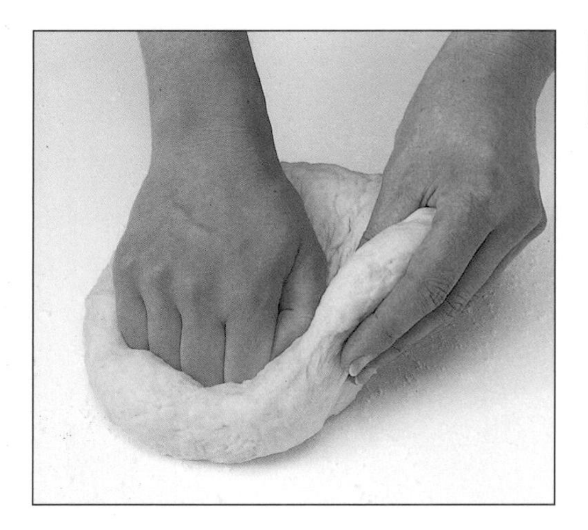

2 Knead the dough on a lightly floured surface for about 5 minutes until it is light and elastic. Place in an oiled polythene bag and leave in a warm place for 1 hour, or until doubled in size. Turn out onto a floured surface and divide into 2 or 4 pieces. Knead each piece lightly.

3 Roll out the dough to cover two 23cm/9 inch or four 15cm/6 inch lightly oiled ovenproof plates. Alternatively, place a piece of dough on each plate and press it out, with floured knuckles, to cover the base.

4 Brush with some of the oil, cover with the tomatoes and season with salt and pepper. Sprinkle with basil and oregano and top with Mozzarella. Sprinkle with Parmesan and a little oil. Leave to rise in a warm place for 30 minutes. Bake in a preheated oven at 220°C/425°F/Gas Mark 7 for 15 minutes, then reduce the heat to 180°C/350°F/Gas Mark 4 for 5 minutes. Serve immediately.

PREPARATION: 2 HOURS
COOKING: 20 MINUTES
SERVES: 4

PREMIUM
NASTRO

PESCE SPADA ALLA PALERMITAN

Swordfish Palermo-style

4 swordfish steaks, about 250g/8oz each
salt
flour
2 garlic cloves
125ml/4 fl oz olive oil
4 anchovy fillets, finely chopped
1 onion, finely chopped
4 tomatoes, skinned, seeded and chopped
pinch of dried rosemary, crumbled
12 green olives, stoned and sliced
1 tablespoon capers
freshly ground black pepper
2 tablespoons chopped fresh parsley

1 Wash the swordfish steaks and pat them dry with kitchen paper. Sprinkle them with salt and then dust lightly with flour on both sides.

2 Fry the garlic cloves in the olive oil over low heat until golden. Discard the garlic and brown the swordfish steaks in the same oil, turning once. Remove and keep warm.

3 Add the anchovies and onion to the oil and fry until golden, and the anchovies are reduced to a purée. Add the tomatoes and rosemary and simmer gently for 30 minutes, until reduced and thickened.

4 Add the olives and capers and season to taste with salt and pepper. Return the swordfish to the sauce and then heat through very gently. Serve them sprinkled with chopped parsley.

PREPARATION: 15 MINUTES
COOKING: 45 MINUTES
SERVES: 4

FRITTO MISTO DI MARE

Fried mixed seafood

1 Make the batter: sift the flour and salt into a mixing bowl and make a well in the centre. Pour in the olive oil and gradually beat in the tepid water to make a smooth, thick batter. Cover the bowl and put in the refrigerator to rest for 2 hours.

2 Immediately before using, whisk the egg white until it forms stiff peaks, and lightly fold the beaten egg white into the batter with a metal spoon. Take care not to beat it into the batter mixture.

PREPARATION: 15 MINUTES
+ 2 HOURS CHILLING TIME
COOKING: 3-6 MINUTES
SERVES: 4

3 Meanwhile, prepare the seafood: wash all the fish and shellfish under running cold water and pat dry. Clean the scallops. Cut the white fish into smallish pieces, and remove any skin and bones. Shell the prawns, leaving the tails intact and removing the black vein running along the back. Dip them in the prepared batter and shake off any excess batter.

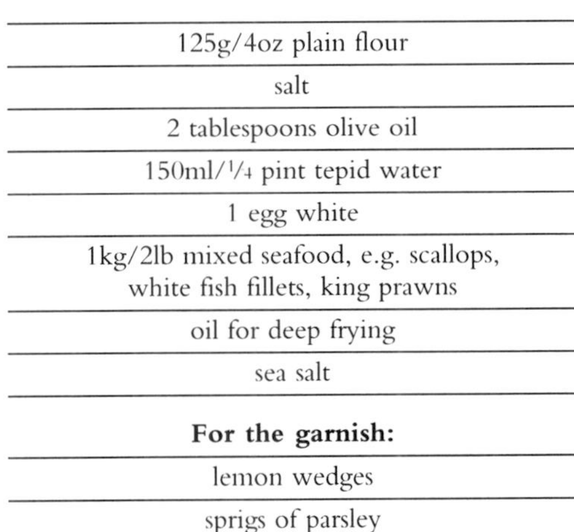

125g/4oz plain flour

salt

2 tablespoons olive oil

150ml/¼ pint tepid water

1 egg white

1kg/2lb mixed seafood, e.g. scallops, white fish fillets, king prawns

oil for deep frying

sea salt

For the garnish:

lemon wedges

sprigs of parsley

4 Heat the oil for deep frying to 190°C/375°F. Cook the battered fish, scallops and prawns for 3-6 minutes, depending on size, or until they are crisp and golden. Lift out and drain on crumpled kitchen paper. Sprinkle with sea salt and pile up on a warm serving dish. Garnish with lemon wedges and parsley and serve immediately.

SOGLIOLE ALLA PARMIGIANA

Sole with Parmesan cheese

1 Skin the Dover soles. Put some flour in a shallow bowl and season with salt and pepper. Dip the soles into the seasoned flour to dust them lightly on both sides. Shake off any excess flour.

2 Heat the butter in a large frying pan. Add the floured Dover soles and cook over gentle heat until they are golden brown on both sides, turning them once during cooking.

PREPARATION: 5 MINUTES
COOKING: 12 MINUTES
SERVES: 4

3 Sprinkle the grated Parmesan cheese over the soles, and then cook very gently for another 2-3 minutes until the cheese melts.

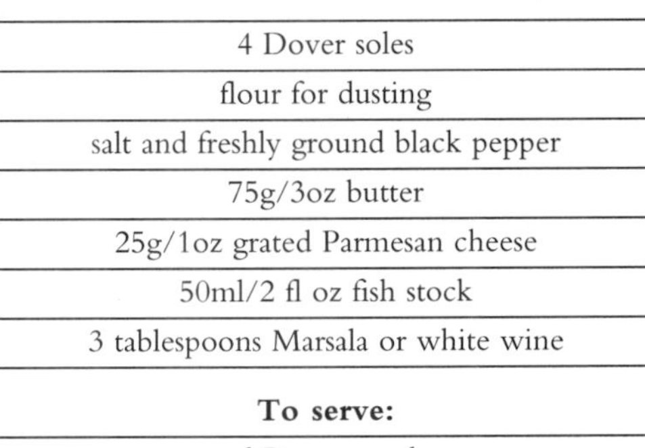

4 Dover soles

flour for dusting

salt and freshly ground black pepper

75g/3oz butter

25g/1oz grated Parmesan cheese

50ml/2 fl oz fish stock

3 tablespoons Marsala or white wine

To serve:

grated Parmesan cheese

lemon wedges

4 Add the fish stock and the Marsala or white wine. Cover the pan and cook over very low heat for 4-5 minutes, until the soles are cooked and tender and the sauce reduced. Serve sprinkled with grated Parmesan, garnished with lemon wedges.

1992
PRODUCED AND BOTTLED IN ITALY
Frascati
SUPERIORE
WILKENS

PESCE ALLA PIZZAIOLA

Fish with tomato and garlic sauce

4 x 150g/5oz white fish steaks, e.g. sea bass, John Dory, monkfish
3 tablespoons olive oil

For the marinade:

5 tablespoons olive oil
juice of 1/2 lemon
1 tablespoon finely chopped fresh parsley

For the tomato sauce:

2 tablespoons olive oil
4 garlic cloves, chopped
750g/1 1/2lb tomatoes, skinned and chopped
4 anchovy fillets, chopped
salt and freshly ground black pepper
1 tablespoon chopped oregano

1 Wash the fish steaks under running cold water and pat dry with absorbent kitchen paper. Put all the marinade ingredients in a bowl and mix well together.

2 Add the white fish steaks to the marinade, turning them until they are thoroughly coated and glistening with oil. Cover the bowl and leave in a cool place for at least 1 hour.

3 Heat the olive oil in a large frying pan. Remove the fish steaks from the marinade and fry gently until they are cooked and golden brown on both sides, turning the fish once during cooking. Remove the steaks from the pan and keep them warm.

4 While the fish steaks are cooking, make the tomato sauce. Heat the olive oil in a pan and sauté the garlic until just golden. Add the tomatoes and chopped anchovies, and cook over medium heat until the tomatoes are reduced to a thick pulpy consistency. Season to taste with salt and pepper. Pour the sauce over the fish and sprinkle with oregano.

PREPARATION: 15 MINUTES +
1 HOUR MARINATING
COOKING: 15 MINUTES
SERVES: 4

TONNO FRESCO ALLA MARINARA

Fresh tuna with tomatoes

4 fresh tuna steaks, about 150g/5oz each
salt and freshly ground black pepper
flour for dusting
3 tablespoons olive oil
1 onion, chopped
2 garlic cloves, crushed
750g/1½lb skinned and chopped tomatoes
2 tablespoons chopped fresh parsley
few basil leaves, chopped
1 bay leaf
4 anchovy fillets, mashed
8 black olives

1 Wash the tuna steaks and pat dry with absorbent kitchen paper. Season with salt and plenty of freshly ground black pepper, and then dust the steaks lightly with flour.

2 Heat half of the olive oil in a large shallow frying pan and sauté the tuna steaks until golden on one side. Flip them over and cook the other side until golden. Carefully remove them from the pan and then transfer to a dish and keep warm.

3 Add the remaining oil to the pan and sauté the onion and garlic for about 5 minutes, until golden and soft. Add the tomatoes, parsley, basil, bay leaf and mashed anchovies and stir well. Bring to the boil and then continue boiling until the mixture reduces and thickens slightly.

4 Return the tuna to the pan, season to taste and simmer gently for 15 minutes, turning once. Turn off the heat, add the olives and leave to stand for 5 minutes. Discard the bay leaf and transfer the tuna steaks in their sauce to a warm serving dish.

PREPARATION: 15 MINUTES
COOKING: 30 MINUTES
SERVES: 4

PESCE ALLA SICILIANA

Sicilian fish stew

1 Prepare the mussels: cover with cold water and discard any which are cracked or open or float to the top. Scrub well to remove any barnacles, remove the beards and soak in fresh cold water until ready to cook.

2 Heat 2 tablespoons of the olive oil in a heavy-based frying pan, and sauté the onion, garlic and carrots for about 5 minutes, or until soft. Add the tomatoes with their juice, the black olives and bay leaf, and season with salt and freshly ground black pepper. Simmer gently for 15 minutes.

3 Cut 4 large circles from the slices of bread. Heat the remaining oil in a small frying pan and then sauté the bread until crisp and golden on both sides. Remove, drain on absorbent kitchen paper and keep warm.

4 Add the prepared fish to the stew and cook for 5 minutes. Add the mussels and simmer for 10 minutes, or until the shells open. Discard any that do not open. Remove the bay leaf. Put a fried bread croûte in the bottom of each of 4 warm deep plates or large shallow soup bowls. Ladle the fish stew over the top. Sprinkle with chopped parsley and serve immediately with plenty of crusty bread.

- 300ml/½ pint mussels
- 75ml/3 fl oz olive oil
- 1 onion, thinly sliced
- 2 garlic cloves, crushed
- 2 carrots, cut into strips
- 425g/14oz canned chopped tomatoes
- 125g/4oz black olives
- 1 bay leaf
- salt and freshly ground black pepper
- 4 slices white bread
- 1kg/2lb mixed fish (e.g. white fish, red mullet, scallops, prawns), prepared or cut into chunks
- 2 tablespoons finely chopped fresh parsley

PREPARATION: 30 MINUTES
COOKING: 35 MINUTES
SERVES: 4

TROTA IN CARTOCCIO

Baked trout parcels

2 tablespoons olive oil
2 garlic cloves, crushed
1 medium onion, chopped
1 celery stick, chopped
salt and freshly ground black pepper
4 sprigs of rosemary
2 tablespoons dry white wine
2 x 375g/12oz trout, cleaned
To garnish:
sprigs of rosemary

1 Heat the olive oil in a frying pan and add the garlic, onion and celery. Fry gently for about 5 minutes until soft and golden. Add some salt and ground black pepper, 2 rosemary sprigs and the white wine. Cook gently for 5 minutes.

2 Cut out 2 double sheets of greaseproof paper large enough to enclose the trout. Brush the paper lightly with a little oil. Divide the sautéed onion mixture equally between the 2 pieces of paper.

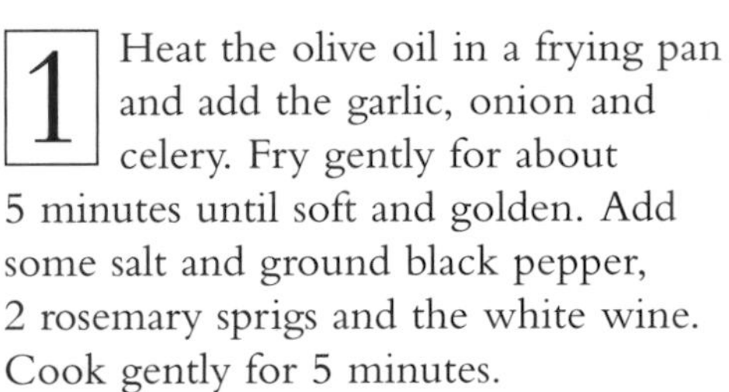

3 Wash the trout and dry well with absorbent kitchen paper. Sprinkle inside and out with salt and freshly ground black pepper. Place one trout on top of the onion mixture on each piece of paper and top with a sprig of rosemary.

4 Fold the paper over the fish and wrap loosely, securing the sides with a double fold and double folding the ends. Place on a baking sheet and cook in a preheated oven at 180°C/350°F/Gas Mark 4 for 20 minutes until the fish is cooked and tender. Remove the fish from the paper and serve garnished with sprigs of rosemary.

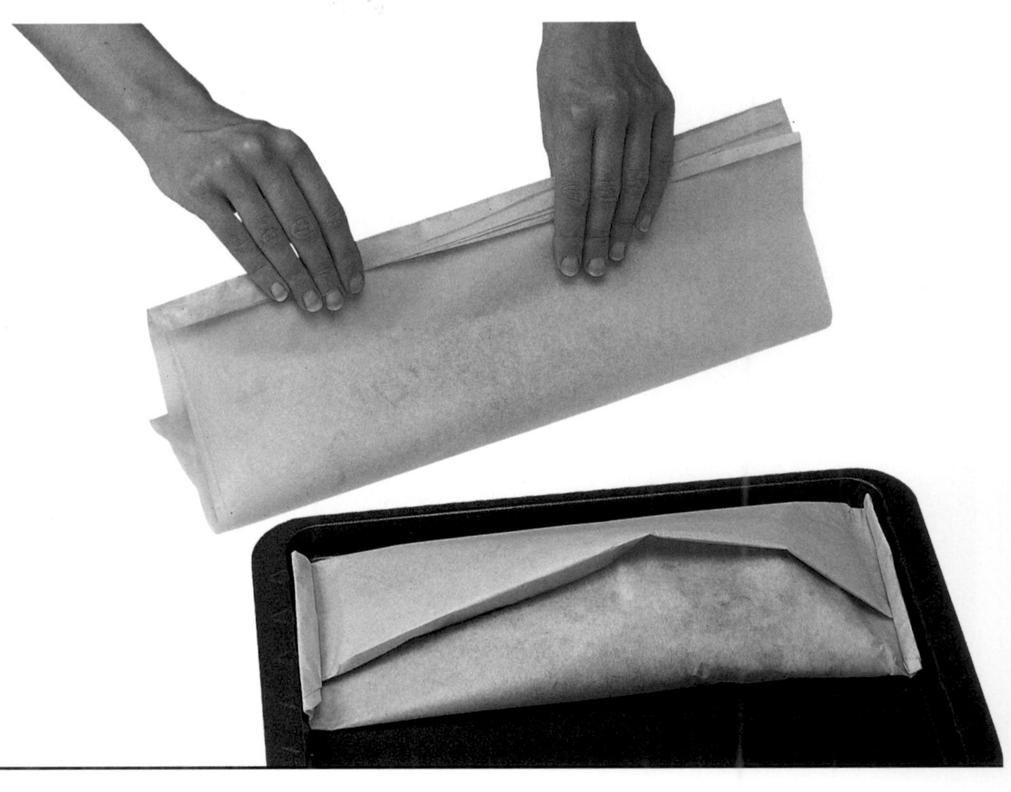

PREPARATION: 10-15 MINUTES
COOKING: 20 MINUTES
SERVES: 2

COZZE ITALIANO

Mussels Italian-style

1 Prepare the mussels: place in a bowl and cover them with cold water. Discard any that are open or rise to the surface. Scrub the mussels to remove any barnacles, and remove the beards. Soak in fresh cold water until ready to cook. Drain well.

2 Put the mussels in a deep saucepan with the bouquet garni, salt and pepper. Add the water and wine, cover the pan and cook over moderate heat until the mussels open, shaking the pan occasionally. Discard any mussels that do not open, then strain them and reserve the liquid.

3 Remove the empty half of each mussel shell, and arrange the remaining shells, mussel-side up, close together in a shallow ovenproof baking dish. Sprinkle with the chopped shallot, garlic, parsley, breadcrumbs and Parmesan cheese.

2.25 litres/4 pints mussels
bouquet garni
salt and freshly ground black pepper
125ml/4 fl oz water
125ml/4 fl oz dry white wine
2 tablespoons finely chopped shallot
1 garlic clove, crushed
2 tablespoons chopped fresh parsley
75g/3oz fresh breadcrumbs
3 tablespoons grated Parmesan cheese
25g/1oz butter

4 Reduce the mussel liquid to half its original volume by boiling rapidly. Pour the reduced liquid around the mussels and dot with butter. Bake in a preheated oven at 180°C/350°F/Gas Mark 4 for 15 minutes. Serve immediately.

PREPARATION: 30 MINUTES
COOKING: 15 MINUTES
SERVES: 4

CARMIGNANO -
VIN RUS
CAPEZZAN

SCALLOPINE ALLA BOLOGNESE

Veal escalopes Bologna-style

1 Beat the escalopes lightly with a rolling pin to thin them out. Sprinkle each one with a little salt and coat them with flour. Preheat the oven to 230°C/450°F/Gas Mark 8, or the grill to high.

3 Cover each escalope with a slice of ham and then top with a slice of cheese. Leave them in a warm place while you deglaze the pan.

2 In a large frying pan, melt the butter and, when foaming, sauté the escalopes on both sides until they are lightly browned and cooked. Arrange them side by side in a buttered ovenproof dish.

4 Add the stock and Marsala to the butter in the frying pan. Bring to the boil, scraping the residues away from the bottom of the pan with a wooden spoon. Pour the sauce over the escalopes, sprinkle with black pepper and place the baking dish in the hot oven or under the grill until the cheese has melted. Serve sprinkled with parsley.

PREPARATION: 10 MINUTES
COOKING: 15-20 MINUTES
SERVES: 4

- 8 small veal escalopes, about 75g/3oz each
- salt
- flour for coating
- 75g/3oz butter
- 8 thin slices Parma ham (prosciutto crudo)
- 8 thin slices Gruyère or Emmenthal cheese
- 3 tablespoons chicken stock
- 3 tablespoons Marsala
- freshly ground black pepper
- 2 tablespoons chopped fresh parsley

SALTIMBOCCA ALLA ROMANA

Veal escalopes with Parma ham and sage

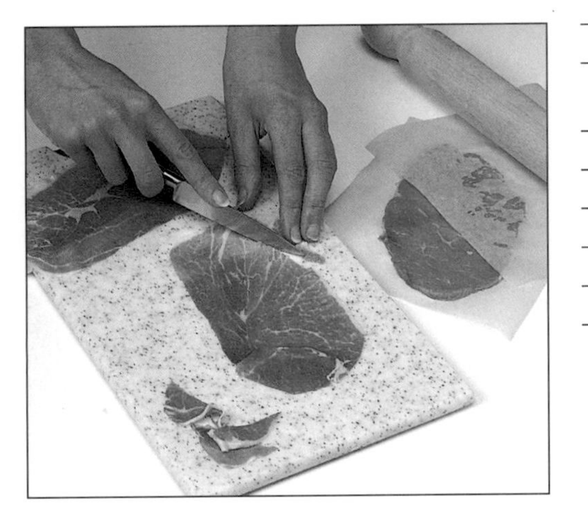

8 small veal escalopes, about 50g/2oz each
8 paper-thin slices of Parma ham (proscuitto crudo)
salt
8 fresh sage leaves
75g/3oz butter
75ml/3 fl oz Marsala or dry white wine
fresh sage leaves to garnish

1 Beat the escalopes out thinly, and trim the slices of ham to about the same size as the escalopes.

2 Sprinkle each escalope with a pinch of salt and place a sage leaf on top. Cover each escalope with a slice of ham, and secure with a cocktail stick. Do not roll them up.

3 Heat 50g/2oz of the butter in a large frying pan and, when foaming, add the escalopes and sauté briskly on both sides until cooked and golden – about 6-8 minutes. Remove and keep warm.

4 Add the Marsala or white wine to the buttery juices left in the pan. Bring to the boil, scraping the bottom of the pan with a wooden spoon and stirring well. Stir in the remaining butter and spoon the sauce over the escalopes. Garnish with fresh sage leaves.

PREPARATION: 10 MINUTES
COOKING: 12-15 MINUTES
SERVES: 4

OSSO BUCO ALLA MILANESE

Braised shin of veal

1 onion, finely chopped
125g/4oz butter
1 meaty shin of veal, sawed into 4 slices, about 6cm/2½ inches thick
flour for dusting
1 carrot, thinly sliced
1 celery stick, thinly sliced
3 tomatoes, skinned and chopped
salt and freshly ground black pepper
2-3 sage leaves
150ml/¼ pint dry white wine

For the gremolata:

4 tablespoons finely chopped parsley
1 garlic clove, crushed
1 anchovy fillet, finely chopped
finely grated rind of ½ lemon

1 Fry the onion in half of the butter in a wide shallow frying pan until it is soft and golden. Dust the slices of veal with flour and then fry them in the same pan, turning several times, until they are golden brown on all sides. Stand them on their sides to prevent the marrow in the bones slipping out during cooking.

PREPARATION: 15 MINUTES
COOKING: 2 HOURS
SERVES: 4

2 Add the carrot, celery and tomatoes. Season with salt and pepper and add the sage leaves. Stir in the wine, then cover the pan and simmer gently for about 1 hour, or until the veal is cooked and tender. Add a few tablespoons of water or a little more wine if the sauce evaporates too quickly.

3 While the veal is cooking, prepare the gremolata. Mix together thoroughly the parsley, garlic, anchovy and finely grated lemon rind in a small bowl until well combined.

4 Spread each piece of veal with a little of the gremolata and cook for a few minutes. Transfer the veal to a heated serving dish and keep warm. Add a few tablespoons of water to the pan juices and bring to the boil, scraping the bottom of the pan clean. Simmer until slightly reduced and thickened. Stir in the remaining butter and, when it has melted, pour over the veal. Serve with risotto.

MESSICANI ALLA MILANESE

Milanese stuffed veal rolls

- 12 small thin slices of veal
- 6 fresh sage leaves
- 2 rashers streaky bacon
- 50g/2oz butter
- 4 tablespoons Marsala
- 4 tablespoons dry white wine
- 3 fresh sage leaves, roughly chopped

For the filling:

- 50g/2oz raw smoked ham (prosciutto crudo), chopped
- 1 chicken liver, finely chopped
- 25g/1oz fresh white breadcrumbs
- 2 tablespoons freshly grated Parmesan cheese
- 1 teaspoon finely chopped parsley
- 1 egg, beaten
- salt and freshly ground black pepper
- 1/4 teaspoon freshly grated nutmeg

1 Make the filling: put the chopped ham, chicken liver, breadcrumbs, Parmesan and parsley in a bowl. Bind together with the beaten egg, and season to taste with salt, pepper and grated nutmeg.

PREPARATION: 15 MINUTES
COOKING: 15 MINUTES
SERVES: 4-6

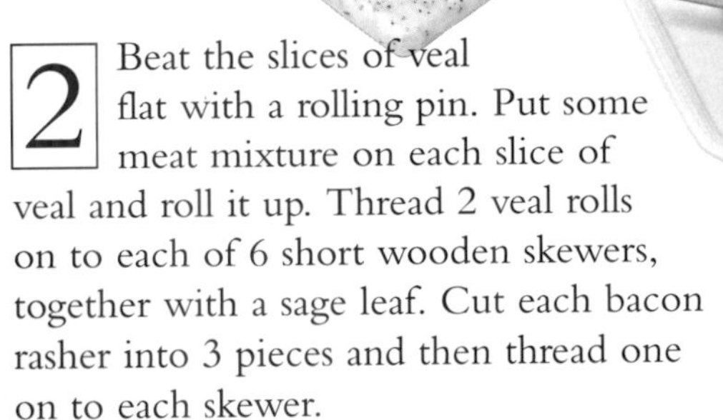

2 Beat the slices of veal flat with a rolling pin. Put some meat mixture on each slice of veal and roll it up. Thread 2 veal rolls on to each of 6 short wooden skewers, together with a sage leaf. Cut each bacon rasher into 3 pieces and then thread one on to each skewer.

3 Heat the butter in a frying pan and then sauté the veal rolls until they are evenly cooked and golden brown, turning occasionally. Remove the veal rolls from the pan and keep warm while you make the sauce.

4 Add the Marsala and wine to the buttery pan juices and bring to the boil, scraping the bottom of the pan clean with a wooden spoon. Add the chopped sage and simmer for 3-5 minutes until reduced slightly. Pour the sauce over the veal rolls and serve immediately.

ARGIANO
BRUNELLO
DI MONTALCINO
1988

BRASATO AL BAROLO

Beef braised in red wine

1.5kg/3lb joint of topside or rolled silverside
1 onion, sliced
1 carrot, sliced
1 celery stick, sliced
2 garlic cloves, crushed
2 bay leaves
6 peppercorns
600ml/1 pint Barolo or other red wine
25g/1oz bacon fat or dripping
1 onion, finely chopped
sprig of rosemary
salt and freshly ground black pepper

1 Put the meat in a deep bowl. Add the sliced onion, carrot, celery, garlic, bay leaves, peppercorns and the red wine. Cover the bowl and place in the refrigerator to marinate for 24 hours, turning the beef several times. Lift the meat out of the marinade and dry it carefully. Reserve the marinade.

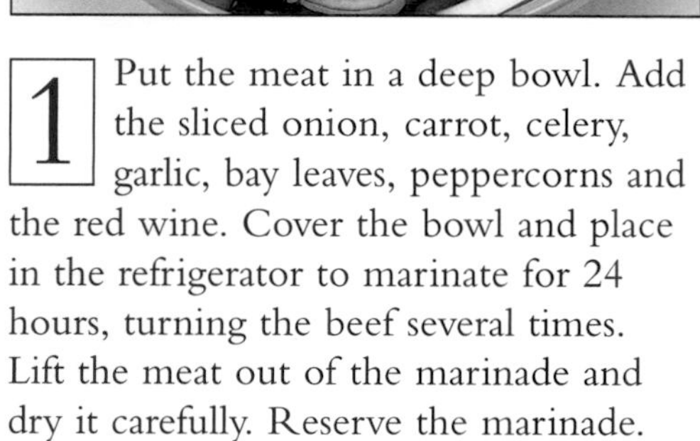

2 Heat the bacon fat or dripping in a large flameproof casserole and sauté the chopped onion over low heat for about 5 minutes, or until it is soft and golden. Put in the beef, increase the heat and brown quickly on all sides.

3 Strain the reserved marinade into the casserole and bring to the boil. Add the rosemary sprig and season with salt and freshly ground black pepper. Lower the heat, cover tightly and simmer very gently for at least 3 hours, or until the meat is tender. Turn the meat once halfway through cooking.

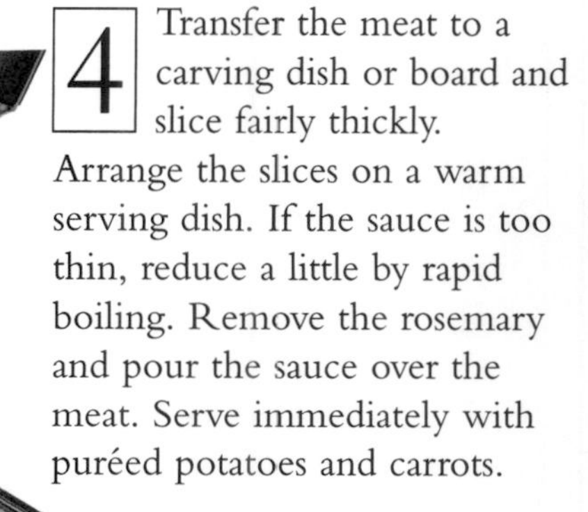

4 Transfer the meat to a carving dish or board and slice fairly thickly. Arrange the slices on a warm serving dish. If the sauce is too thin, reduce a little by rapid boiling. Remove the rosemary and pour the sauce over the meat. Serve immediately with puréed potatoes and carrots.

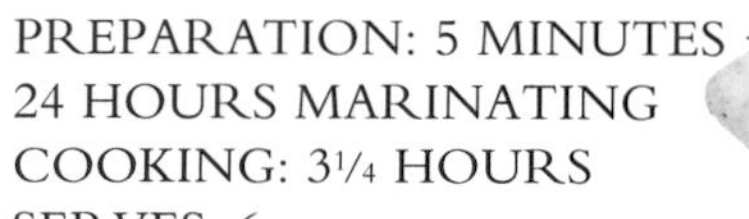

PREPARATION: 5 MINUTES + 24 HOURS MARINATING
COOKING: 3¼ HOURS
SERVES: 6

VENDEMMIA
1987
G.DAMILANO
BAROLO
V.Q.P.R.D.

INVOLTINI AL SUGO

Stuffed beef olives

1kg/2lb beef topside
salt and freshly ground black pepper
125g/4oz grated Pecorino cheese
2 slices raw ham (prosciutto crudo), chopped
3 garlic cloves, crushed
3 tablespoons chopped fresh parsley
1 tablespoon chopped fresh basil
3 tablespoons olive oil
few basil leaves, torn

For the tomato sauce:

1 onion, chopped
2 garlic cloves, crushed
1kg/2lb tomatoes, skinned and chopped
1 tablespoon tomato paste
125ml/4 fl oz red wine
salt and freshly ground black pepper

1 Cut the beef into thin slices and place between 2 sheets of greaseproof paper. Flatten them with a rolling pin and then season with salt and ground black pepper.

2 Make the filling: put the grated Pecorino cheese in a bowl with the chopped ham, garlic, parsley and basil. Mix well together and spread a little of this mixture on to each slice of beef. Roll up, folding in the sides, and secure with cotton or fine string.

3 Heat the olive oil in a large saucepan and gently fry the beef rolls until they are slightly brown all over, turning as necessary. Remove from the pan and keep warm.

4 Make the sauce: add the onion and garlic to the oil in the pan and sauté until soft. Add the tomatoes, tomato paste, wine and seasoning. Bring to the boil, and then add the beef rolls. Cover and simmer gently for 1½-2 hours, or until tender. Remove the string from the beef rolls and serve with the sauce, sprinkled with basil.

PREPARATION: 20 MINUTES
COOKING: 1½-2 HOURS
SERVES: 6

FEGATO ALLA VENEZIANA

Calves' liver Venetian-style

1 Heat the olive oil and butter together in a large heavy-based frying pan. Add the onions and simmer gently over very low heat, stirring occasionally, for about 40 minutes, or until the onions are soft, golden and translucent but not browned. Remove the onions with a slotted spoon and keep warm.

2 Add the thinly sliced calves' liver to the pan and fry very quickly until brown on one side. Turn over and quickly cook the other side. The liver should be lightly browned on the outside and still pink in the middle. Remove and keep warm.

3 Add the veal or chicken stock and vinegar to the pan and bring to the boil, scraping the bottom of the pan with a wooden spoon and stirring until the sauce reduces. Season to taste with salt and ground black pepper, and stir in the chopped parsley.

- 6 tablespoons olive oil
- 1 tablespoon butter
- 4 medium-sized onions, thinly sliced
- 625g/1¼lb calves' liver, thinly sliced
- 4 tablespoons veal or chicken stock
- 1 tablespoon wine vinegar
- salt
- freshly ground black pepper
- 2 tablespoons finely chopped parsley

4 Arrange the liver and onions on a heated serving dish or 4 serving plates, and pour the sauce over the top. Serve with a bowl of fresh pasta and a crisp green salad.

PREPARATION: 10 MINUTES
COOKING: 50 MINUTES
SERVES: 4

POLLO ALLA CACCIATORA

Hunter's chicken

4 tablespoons olive oil
4 slices pancetta or unsmoked bacon, chopped
1 large chicken, about 1.5kg/3lb, cut into 4 portions
2 garlic cloves, crushed
2 red onions, roughly chopped
500g/1lb tomatoes, skinned and chopped
250g/8oz mushrooms, sliced
sprig of rosemary
1 bay leaf
150ml/¼ pint dry white wine
300ml/½ pint chicken stock
salt and pepper

1 Heat the oil in a large frying pan and fry the pancetta or bacon for 2-3 minutes, until lightly browned. Stir occasionally to prevent the pancetta sticking. Remove and keep warm.

2 Put the chicken portions in the pan and sauté in the oil, turning occasionally, until they are golden brown all over.

3 Remove the chicken from the pan and keep warm. Add the garlic, onions, tomatoes and mushrooms, and cook gently over low heat for 5 minutes, stirring occasionally. Return the chicken pieces to the frying pan.

4 Add the herbs, then pour in the wine and chicken stock. Simmer gently for about 1 hour, until the chicken is tender and the sauce reduced. Season to taste with salt and pepper.

PREPARATION: 15 MINUTES
COOKING: 1¼ HOURS
SERVES: 4

Chianti Rufina
DENOMINAZIONE DI ORIGINE CONTROLLATA
RISERVA 1977
VILLA DI VETRICE
PRODUCE OF ITALY

PETTI DI POLLO RIPIENI

Stuffed chicken breasts

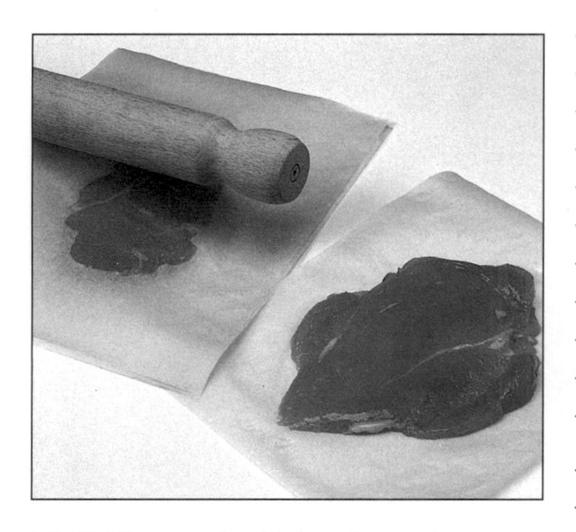

4 chicken breasts, skinned and boned
salt and freshly ground black pepper
4 thin small slices Parma ham (prosciutto crudo)
4 thin slices Bel Paese cheese
4 cooked or canned asparagus spears
flour for dusting
50g/2oz butter
1 tablespoon olive oil
6 tablespoons Marsala or dry white wine
2 tablespoons chicken stock

To garnish:
cooked or canned asparagus spears

1 Place each chicken breast between 2 sheets of damp greaseproof paper and then beat with a rolling pin until thin. Season lightly with salt and freshly ground black pepper.

2 Place a slice of ham on top of each beaten chicken breast, then a slice of cheese and, finally, an asparagus spear. Roll each breast up and wind a piece of cotton around to hold it. Tie securely and dust with flour.

3 Heat 25g/1oz of the butter with the oil in a frying pan. Sauté the chicken rolls over very low heat, turning them frequently, for about 15 minutes, or until tender, cooked and golden. Remove the cotton, and transfer the rolls to a serving dish and keep warm.

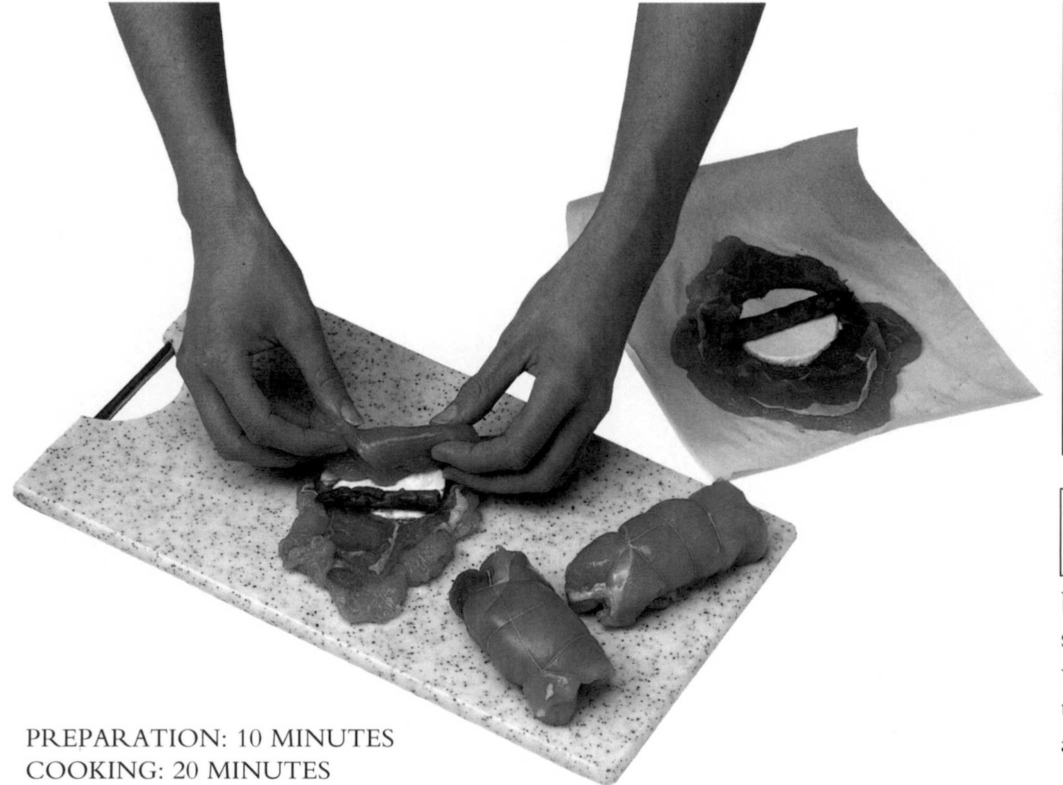

4 Add the Marsala or wine, chicken stock and the remaining butter to the juices in the pan. Bring to the boil and simmer for 3-4 minutes, scraping the base of the pan with a wooden spoon. Spoon the sauce over the chicken and serve garnished with asparagus spears.

PREPARATION: 10 MINUTES
COOKING: 20 MINUTES
SERVES: 4

POLLO CON POLENTA

Tuscan chicken with polenta

4 tablespoons olive oil
1 chicken, jointed
1 onion, chopped
5 plum tomatoes, skinned and chopped
300ml/½ pint dry white wine
sprig of rosemary
1 tablespoon chopped fresh thyme
salt and freshly ground black pepper
15g/½oz flour blended with 15g/½ oz butter
2 tablespoons chopped fresh parsley

For the polenta:

1.8 litres/3 pints water
salt
300g/10oz polenta
15g/½oz butter
freshly ground black pepper

1 Heat the olive oil in a large heavy-based frying pan and sauté the chicken joints until golden brown all over, turning occasionally. Remove and keep warm.

2 Add the onion to the pan and cook gently until soft and golden. Add the chopped tomatoes, white wine, rosemary, thyme and salt and pepper. Bring to the boil, stirring, and then reduce the heat to a simmer. Return the chicken to the pan and then simmer, covered, for 20-30 minutes until the chicken is cooked.

3 Meanwhile, make the polenta: put the cold water, salt and polenta in a large saucepan and stir thoroughly with a wooden spoon. Bring slowly to the boil, stirring continuously, and then reduce the heat to a simmer. Continue stirring over low heat for 15-20 minutes until the polenta is thick and smooth and has absorbed all the liquid. Stir in the butter and season with black peper.

4 Remove the chicken and arrange on a heated serving dish. Add the blended flour and butter (beurre manié) to the sauce and bring to the boil, stirring constantly, until the sauce thickens slightly. Pour over the chicken, sprinkle with parsley and serve with the polenta.

PREPARATION: 15 MINUTES
COOKING: 45 MINUTES
SERVES: 4

PARMIGIANA DI MELANZANE

Baked aubergines with cheese

1.5kg/3lb aubergines
salt
125ml/4 fl oz olive oil
1 onion, finely chopped
2kg/4lb tomatoes, skinned and chopped
3 fresh basil leaves, torn, or 2 teaspoons dried basil
freshly ground black pepper
flour for dusting
150g/5oz grated Parmesan cheese
250g/8oz Mozzarella cheese, thinly sliced

1 Trim the stems from the aubergines and slice them into rounds - not lengthwise. Sprinkle each slice with a little salt and place the salted slices in a colander. Cover with a plate and weight it down. Leave the aubergines to drain for about 30 minutes.

2 Meanwhile, make the tomato sauce: heat 4 tablespoons of the olive oil in a heavy pan, and fry the onion until soft and golden. Add the chopped tomatoes and basil, mix well and simmer gently, uncovered, until the mixture reduces to a thick sauce. Season to taste with salt and pepper.

PREPARATION: 40 MINUTES
COOKING: 1 HOUR
SERVES: 4

3 Rinse the aubergine slices thoroughly in cold water to remove the saltiness. Pat dry with absorbent kitchen paper and dust them with flour. Heat a little of the remaining olive oil in a large frying pan and fry the aubergine in batches, adding more oil as needed, until they are cooked and golden brown on both sides. Drain on absorbent kitchen paper.

4 Oil an ovenproof dish and arrange a layer of aubergine slices in the bottom of the dish. Sprinkle with Parmesan cheese and cover with Mozzarella cheese slices. Spoon some of the tomato sauce over the top and continue layering up in this way until all the ingredients are used up, ending with a layer of tomato sauce and Parmesan cheese. Bake in a preheated oven at 200°C/400°F/Gas Mark 6 for 30 minutes. Serve hot, warm or cold.

ZUCCHINI RIPIENI

Stuffed courgettes

1 Trim the ends from the courgettes and cook in a large saucepan of boiling salted water for 5 minutes. Drain well. Soak the bread in a little milk until soft and then squeeze dry.

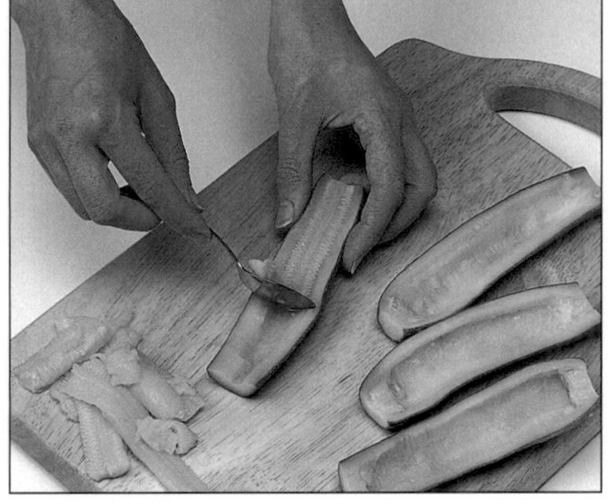

2 Cut the courgettes in half lengthwise and carefully scoop out the centres, using a teaspoon. You should be left with long boat-shaped cases which are ready for filling.

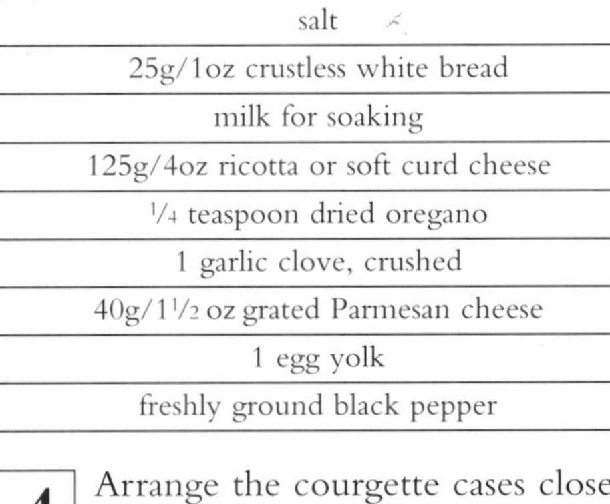

6 courgettes
salt
25g/1oz crustless white bread
milk for soaking
125g/4oz ricotta or soft curd cheese
1/4 teaspoon dried oregano
1 garlic clove, crushed
40g/1 1/2 oz grated Parmesan cheese
1 egg yolk
freshly ground black pepper

3 Chop the courgette centres finely and put into a bowl. Add the bread, ricotta, oregano, garlic, Parmesan, egg yolk, salt and freshly ground black pepper. Mix thoroughly. The consistency should be fairly soft. If it is too stiff, add a little milk.

4 Arrange the courgette cases close together in a single layer in a well oiled shallow baking tray or ovenproof dish. Fill the cases with the ricotta mixture, and bake in a preheated oven at 190°C/375°F/Gas Mark 5 for 35-40 minutes until the courgettes are tender and the filling is golden brown. Serve immediately.

PREPARATION: 20 MINUTES
COOKING: 35-40 MINUTES
SERVES: 4

BIANCO
DI
CUSTOZA
DENOMINAZIONE DI ORIGINE
1992
PRODUCE OF ITALY

CAPONATA

Sicilian-style aubergines

1 Put the diced aubergine in a colander, sprinkle with salt and leave to drain for 15-20 minutes to exude their bitter juices. Rinse under running cold water to remove any salt and pat dry with kitchen paper.

2 Soak the anchovies in a little warm water in a bowl to remove some of their saltiness. Remove, pat dry and cut the anchovies into thin strips. Set aside.

PREPARATION: 40 MINUTES
COOKING: 1 HOUR
SERVES: 4

3 Sauté the onion in the olive oil until soft and golden. Add the celery and cook for a further 2-3 minutes. Add the aubergine and cook gently for 3 minutes, stirring occasionally, until golden. Add the passata and cook gently until it has been absorbed by the aubergine. Add the wine vinegar and continue cooking for 1 minute. Add the peppers, anchovies, capers and olives and cook for 3 minutes.

- 3 aubergines cut into 1.25cm/½ inch dice
- salt
- 50g/2oz anchovy fillets
- 1 onion, thinly sliced
- 4 tablespoons olive oil
- 2 sticks celery, diced
- 150ml/¼ pint passata (sieved tomatoes)
- 3 tablespoons wine vinegar
- 1 yellow pepper, seeded and thinly sliced
- 1 red pepper, seeded and thinly sliced
- 50g/2oz capers, roughly chopped
- 50g/2oz black olives, pitted and sliced
- 50g/2oz green olives, pitted and sliced
- 2 tablespoons pine nuts
- 2 tablespoons chopped parsley

4 Transfer the mixture to an ovenproof dish and bake, covered, in a preheated oven at 180°C/350°F/Gas Mark 4 for about 1 hour. After 40 minutes, stir in the pine nuts and return to the oven for the remaining 20 minutes. Serve lukewarm or cold sprinkled with chopped parsley. The flavours improve if made a day in advance.

CROSTATA DI SPINACI

Savoury spinach tart

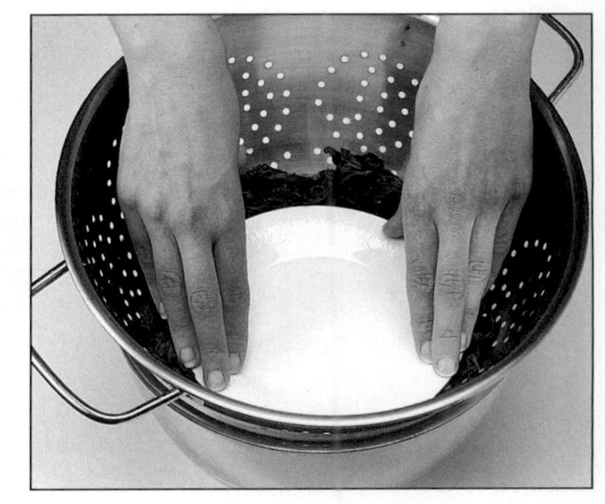

1 Sift the flour and salt into a mixing bowl and rub in the butter. Mix in the egg yolk and sufficient iced water to make a soft dough. Knead lightly until smooth. Leave in the refrigerator for at least 30 minutes to rest. Roll out the pastry to line a 25cm/10 inch flan ring.

2 Prick the base of the pastry case with a fork. Fill with greaseproof paper and baking beans, and bake 'blind' in a preheated oven at 200°C/ 400°F/Gas Mark 6 for 15 minutes. Remove the baking beans and paper and then return to the oven for a further 5 minutes to cook the base.

3 Make the filling: cook the spinach in a little salted water for 3 minutes until softened but still a fresh bright green colour. Drain in a colander and squeeze out any excess water by pressing down hard with a plate. Chop the drained spinach.

250g/8oz plain flour
pinch of salt
125g/4oz butter
1 egg yolk
2-3 tablespoons iced water

For the filling:

250g/8oz small, tender spinach leaves
375g/12oz ricotta cheese
4 eggs, beaten
salt and freshly ground black pepper
grated nutmeg
75ml/3 fl oz single cream
25g/1oz grated Parmesan cheese

PREPARATION: 30 MINUTES + 30 MINUTES CHILLING
COOKING: 30 MINUTES
SERVES: 8

4 Put the ricotta in a bowl and beat in the eggs, salt and pepper and nutmeg. Beat in the cream and continue beating until smooth. Spoon the filling into the pastry case and smooth the top. Sprinkle with Parmesan and bake at 180°C/350°F/Gas Mark 4 for 30 minutes until risen, set and golden brown.

GNOCCHI AL PESTO

Gnocchi with basil sauce

1 Make the pesto: chop the basil and pine nuts roughly and put into a mortar with the garlic, salt and pepper. Pound together until reduced to a thick paste. Transfer to a bowl, add the oil, a little at a time, stirring constantly until thick. Stir in the lemon juice and Parmesan cheese, cover and set aside.

2 Make the gnocchi: drain the potatoes well and shake over the heat to dry them thoroughly. Mash them very finely so that there are no lumps. Beat in the flour, egg, salt, pepper and nutmeg. Mix to a dough and turn out on to a floured board.

PREPARATION: 25 MINUTES
COOKING: 15 MINUTES
SERVES: 4

500g/1lb potatoes, freshly boiled
175g/6oz plain flour
1 egg, beaten
salt and freshly ground black pepper
grated nutmeg

For the pesto sauce:

50g/2oz fresh basil leaves
25g/1oz pine nuts
2 garlic cloves
salt and freshly ground black pepper
4 tablespoons olive oil
juice of 1/2 lemon
40g/1 1/2oz grated Parmesan cheese

To serve:

25g/1oz butter
grated Parmesan cheese

3 With floured hands, roll small pieces of the dough into small croquettes, about the thickness of your thumb. Press them lightly with the prongs of a fork – this will help them to hold the pesto sauce.

4 Bring some salted water to the boil in a large pan. Drop the gnocchi, a few at a time, into the boiling water and cook for 3-5 minutes. They will rise to the surface and float when they are cooked. Remove and drain. Arrange the gnocchi in a buttered serving dish and dot with butter and sprinkle with Parmesan cheese. Pour the pesto sauce over the top.

POJER E SANDRI
Chardonnay

CASSATA ALLA SICILIANA

Sicilian cheesecake

1 Make the sponge: whisk the egg yolks with the sugar, lemon rind and 3 tablespoons of hot water until light and foamy. Sift the flour and baking powder together and fold it gently into the egg yolk mixture.

2 Whisk the egg whites until they are stiff, but not dry. Fold them into the sponge mixture. Pour the mixture into a buttered 25cm/10 inch spring-form cake tin and bake in a preheated oven at 190°C/375°F/Gas Mark 5 for 15-20 minutes, or until the cake is golden and springs back when pressed. Turn out and cool.

PREPARATION: 40 MINUTES
COOKING: 15-20 MINUTES
CHILLING: 2-3 HOURS
SERVES: 6-8

3 Make the filling: dissolve the sugar in 3 tablespoons of water over low heat. Beat the syrup with the ricotta cheese until well blended. Chop half of the fruit coarsely. Beat the cinnamon into the ricotta mixture, and put aside a few tablespoons for decoration. Stir the chopped fruit and chocolate into the rest of the mixture.

3 eggs, separated
125g/4oz caster sugar
finely grated rind of 1/2 lemon
125g/4oz plain flour
1 teaspoon baking powder

For the filling:

175g/6oz caster sugar
750g/1 1/2lb ricotta cheese
500g/1lb mixed crystallized fruit
1/8 teaspoon ground cinnamon
75g/3oz plain chocolate, chopped in small pieces
8 tablespoons Maraschino liqueur

4 Line the base of the cake tin with greaseproof paper. Cut the sponge in half horizontally and put one layer on the base, cut-side up. Sprinkle with half of the Maraschino, and spread with the ricotta mixture. Place the other sponge layer on top and sprinkle with the remaining Maraschino. Fit the ring of the tin in position and chill for several hours. To serve, remove from the tin, coat the top and sides with the reserved ricotta mixture and decorate with the reserved whole fruit.

CARPENE'
PROSECCO

ZABAGLIONE

Whipped wine custard

4 egg yolks
5 tablespoons sugar
8 tablespoons Marsala or sweat white wine

1 Separate the eggs and put the egg yolks in the top of a double-boiler, or in a basin sitting over a small saucepan of gently simmering water. Make sure that the basin is not in contact with the water below.

2 Add the sugar and Marsala or dry white wine, if using, to the egg yolks and stir well.

3 Beat the mixture with either a wire whisk or a hand-held electric whisk until the zabaglione is thick, light and hot. Even with an electric whisk, this will take 10-15 minutes so be patient. Check that the water simmers gently underneath and does not boil dry.

4 When the zabaglione is cooked, pour it carefully into 4 tall glasses and serve immediately. To serve it cold, continue beating the mixture, off the heat, until it has cooled down completely. Mix the cold zabaglione with raspberries or sliced strawberries or peaches if wished.

PREPARATION: 2-3 MINUTES
COOKING: 10-15 MINUTES
SERVES: 4

V.C.A.
MARSALA
FINE
ITALIA I.P.
CASA FONDATA NEL 1875
MARSALA

PANETTONE

Italian fruit cake

50g/2oz caster sugar
25g/1oz fresh yeast
150ml/¼ pint lukewarm water
3 egg yolks
salt
425g/14oz strong plain flour
125g/4oz butter, softened
50g/2oz sultanas
50g/2oz raisins
50g/2oz chopped mixed peel
25g/1oz butter, melted

1 Stir 1 teaspoon of the sugar and all of the yeast into the lukewarm water. Leave to stand for about 10 minutes until frothy. Beat the egg yolks in a large bowl and stir in the yeast mixture, salt and remaining sugar. Beat in 250g/8oz of the flour and then gradually beat in the softened butter, a little at a time. Knead in the remaining flour to make a dough.

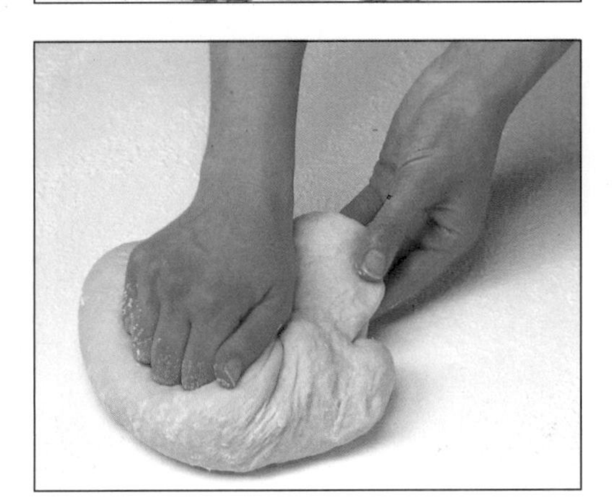

2 Turn the dough out on to a lightly floured surface and knead well until the dough is firm and elastic. Place in a lightly oiled polythene bag and leave in a warm place until well risen and doubled in size.

PREPARATION: 1½ HOURS
COOKING: 40 - 50 MINUTES
SERVES: 10

3 Turn the dough out on to a floured surface and knead in the sultanas, raisins and peel. Continue kneading until the fruit is evenly distributed. Place the dough in a greased 18cm/7 inch round cake tin, and cover with some oiled cling film. Leave in a warm place until the dough rises to the top of the tin.

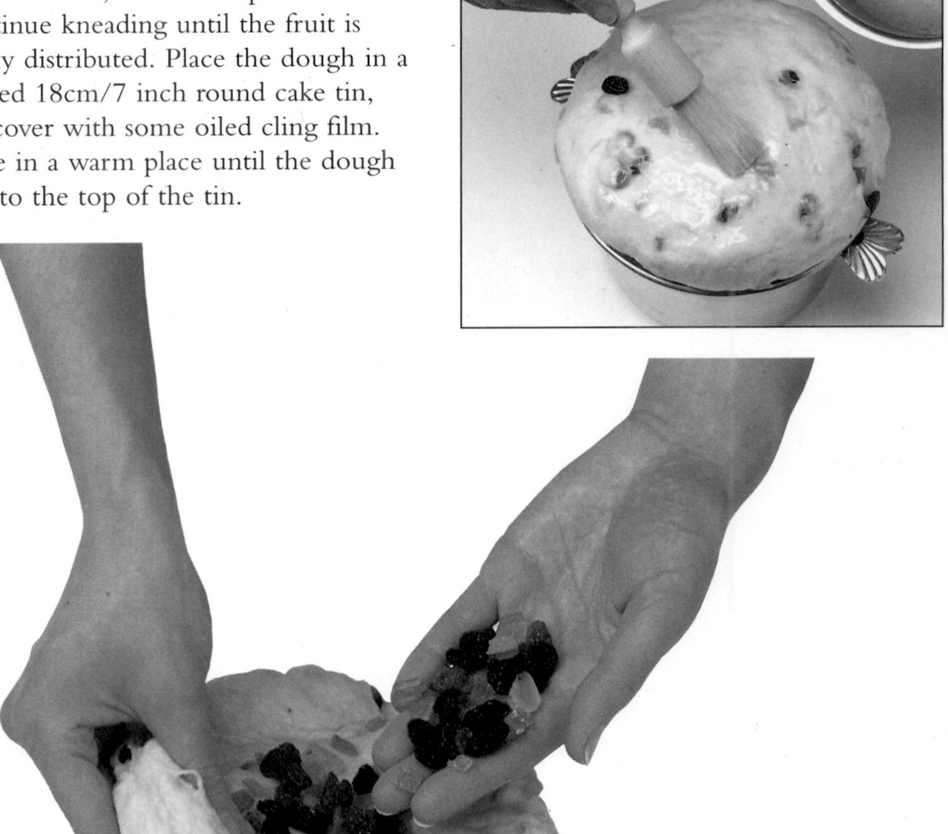

4 Remove the cling film, and brush the top of the dough with some of the melted butter. Bake in a preheated oven at 200°C/400°F/Gas Mark 6 for 20 minutes. Reduce the oven temperature to 180°C/350°F/Gas Mark 4 and cook for a further 20-30 minutes. Remove from the tin and brush the top and sides with the remaining melted butter. Serve warm or cold cut into thin slices.

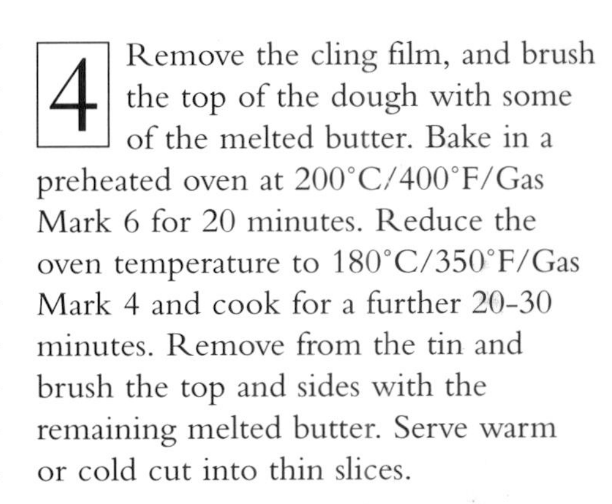

CROSTATA DI RICOTTA

Neapolitan curd tart

250g/8oz plain flour
pinch of salt
125g/4oz butter
1 egg yolk
2-3 tablespoons iced water
icing sugar for dusting
For the filling:
375g/12oz ricotta cheese
75g/3oz caster sugar
3 eggs, well beaten
50g/2oz blanched almonds, finely chopped
75g/3oz chopped mixed peel
finely grated rind of ½ lemon
juice and finely grated rind of ½ orange
¼ teaspoon vanilla essence

1 Sift the flour and salt into a mixing bowl and rub in the butter until the mixture resembles fine breadcrumbs. Mix in the egg yolk and enough iced water to form a soft dough. Knead lightly and leave to chill in the refrigerator for 30 minutes. Roll out the pastry to line a 20cm/8 inch flan ring. Reserve the pastry trimmings.

2 Make the filling: rub the ricotta cheese through a sieve into a basin and then beat in the sugar. Gradually beat in the eggs, and then add the almonds, peel, lemon and orange rind and juice and the vanilla, beating well between each addition.

3 Pour the ricotta cheese filling into the prepared pastry case and then smooth over the surface.

4 Roll out the reserved pastry trimmings and then, using a fluted roller, cut into thin 1cm/½ inch wide strips. Arrange them in a criss-cross pattern over the top of the flan. Bake in the centre of a preheated oven at 180°C/350°F/Gas Mark 4 for 45-50 minutes, or until set and golden. Cool and serve cold, rather than chilled, dusted with icing sugar.

PREPARATION: 20 MINUTES + 30 MINUTES CHILLING
COOKING: 45-50 MINUTES
SERVES: 6-8

ARANCE GLASSATE

Caramelized oranges

12 oranges
175g/6oz sugar
125ml/4 fl oz water

1 Thinly pare the rind from one of the oranges and cut it into fine strips. Cook the strips in a small pan of boiling water for 2-3 minutes, or until softened. Drain well and put aside.

2 Carefully remove all the pith and peel from the oranges with a sharp knife and put them in a large heatproof bowl. Sprinkle the strips of orange rind over the top.

3 Put the sugar and water in a saucepan and heat gently, stirring constantly, until the sugar dissolves completely. Bring to the boil and boil hard until the syrup changes to a rich golden caramel. Take care that the caramel does not become too dark as it will continue to cook after the pan is removed from the heat. If it is too thick, stand well back and add 2 tablespoons of hot water and stir well.

4 Pour the caramel over the oranges and set aside to cool. Put in the refrigerator and leave to chill overnight. To serve, transfer the oranges and caramel to an attractive serving dish and serve with whipped cream. Note: if wished, the oranges can be thinly sliced and secured with cocktail sticks before adding the caramel.

PREPARATION: 15 MINUTES
COOKING: 8-10 MINUTES + CHILLING TIME
SERVES: 6

SOUFFLE DI AMARETTO

Amaretto almond soufflés

4 macaroons
75ml/3 fl oz Amaretto di Saronno
150ml/¼ pint milk
1 drop vanilla essence
15g/½oz butter
25g/1oz strong plain white flour
4 egg yolks (1 kept separately)
4 egg whites
25g/1oz caster sugar
sifted icing sugar to decorate

For the almond purée:
75g/3oz flaked almonds
150ml/¼ pint milk
2 teaspoons sugar

2 Grease and flour four 7.5cm/3 inch individual soufflé dishes. Soak the macaroons in half of the Amaretto and put one macaroon, cut into quarters, in each prepared soufflé dish.

1 Make the almond purée: put the almonds, milk and sugar in a saucepan and bring to the boil. Reduce the heat and simmer gently for a few minutes. Cool slightly and then blend in a food processor or blender until thoroughly mixed.

3 Make the soufflé: put two-thirds of the milk in a heavy saucepan with the vanilla and butter and bring to the boil. Remove from the heat and stir in the remaining milk with the flour and one egg yolk. Heat again until the mixture thickens and whisk briefly. Add the remaining egg yolks and cook for 2 minutes over low heat.

4 Whisk the egg whites until stiff and then whisk in the sugar. Blend the soufflé mixture with the almond purée and remaining Amaretto. Carefully fold in the beaten egg whites. Spoon this mixture into the soufflé dishes and cook in a preheated oven at 220°C/425°F/Gas Mark 7 for 10-12 minutes. Dust with icing sugar.

PREPARATION: 25 MINUTES
COOKING: 10-12 MINUTES
SERVES: 4

TIRAMISU

Mascarpone coffee dessert

1 Mix the egg yolks and sugar together in a bowl, beating with a wooden spoon until they are creamy. Add the vanilla and fold in the mascarpone cheese. The mixture should be thick and creamy.

2 Make the strong black coffee in a jug or cafétière, then mix with the Marsala and brandy in a bowl. Quickly dip the sponge fingers in the coffee mixture. They should absorb just enough liquid to flavour them without going soggy and falling apart.

PREPARATION: 20 MINUTES
CHILLING: 3-4 HOURS
SERVES: 6

3 Arrange some of the soaked sponge fingers in the base of a large attractive glass serving bowl or 4 individual serving dishes. Cover with a layer of the mascarpone mixture.

- 2 egg yolks
- 2 tablespoons caster sugar
- few drops of vanilla essence
- 250g/8oz mascarpone cheese
- 175ml/6 fl oz strong black coffee
- 2 tablespoons Marsala
- 1 tablespoon brandy
- 150g/5oz sponge fingers
- 1 tablespoon cocoa powder
- 2 tablespoons grated dark chocolate

4 Continue layering alternate layers of sponge fingers and mascarpone, finishing with a top layer of mascarpone. Sift the cocoa over the top and sprinkle with grated chocolate. Chill in the refrigerator for 3-4 hours or until set. The flavour improves if the tiramisu is left overnight.

FATTORIA
SELVAPIANA

SAUCES, BREAD AND CROUTONS

RAGU

Bolognese meat sauce

4 tablespoons olive oil
1 onion, finely chopped
1 garlic clove, crushed
4 rashers streaky bacon, rind removed and chopped
1 carrot, diced
1 celery stick, diced
500g/1lb minced beef
125g/4oz chicken livers, chopped
150ml/¼ pint red wine
salt and freshly ground black pepper
125ml/4 fl oz milk
pinch of ground nutmeg
3 tablespoons tomato paste
425g/14oz canned chopped tomatoes

Heat the oil in a saucepan and add the onion, garlic, bacon, carrot and celery. Cook until tender and golden brown. Add the minced beef and chopped chicken livers, and continue cooking over medium heat, stirring occasionally, until evenly brown. Add the red wine and seasoning and bring to the boil. Reduce the heat slightly and cook over medium heat until most of the wine has evaporated. Add the milk and nutmeg and cook gently until absorbed by the meat. Stir in the tomato paste and chopped tomatoes, and simmer very gently for at least 1 hour until the sauce is reduced and richly coloured.

SALSA DI POMODORO

Tomato sauce

2 tablespoons olive oil
1 onion, finely chopped
1 garlic clove, crushed
1kg/2lb tomatoes, skinned and chopped
salt and freshly ground black pepper
pinch of sugar
few basil leaves, chopped

Heat the olive oil in a saucepan and add the onion and garlic. Fry gently until soft and golden. Add the tomatoes and cook gently for 10-15 minutes, until the sauce thickens and reduces. Season with salt and pepper and a pinch of sugar. Just before serving, stir in the chopped basil. Serve with meat, fish or pasta.

SALSA PER INSALATA

Salad dressing

6 tablespoons fruity green olive oil
2 tablespoons lemon juice or vinegar
pinch of salt
1 garlic clove, crushed(optional)
2 anchovy fillets, crushed(optional)

Mix the olive oil with the lemon juice or vinegar and blend thoroughly. Add the salt and the garlic and anchovy fillets(if using).

Variations: add chopped fresh basil or parsley, chopped shallots or onion to vary the flavour.

SALSA DI POMODORO CRUDA

Fresh uncooked tomato sauce

500g/1lb tomatoes, skinned and chopped
1 small onion, finely chopped
1 garlic clove, crushed
50ml/2 fl oz olive oil
salt and freshly ground black pepper
1 tablespoon chopped fresh basil

Mix all the ingredients together in a bowl until thoroughly blended. Let the sauce stand for 1 hour, preferably at room temperature. Serve with pasta.

MAIONESE

Mayonnaise

2 egg yolks
½ teaspoon salt
250ml/8 fl oz olive oil
1 teaspoon lemon juice

Put the egg yolks in a bowl and beat well with a whisk or a hand-held electric whisk until they are pale and creamy. Beat in the salt and then start adding the olive oil, drop by drop. Continue beating all the time and, as the mayonnaise starts to thicken, add the oil in a thin but steady stream, still beating. Beat in the lemon juice last of all, and then check the seasoning, adding more salt if necessary. For success, all the ingredients and utensils should be at room temperature.

Bruschetta

Garlic bread

8 thick slices wholemeal or coarse white bread
4 garlic cloves, peeled
6 tablespoons fruity green olive oil
salt and freshly ground black pepper

Toast the bread under a hot grill until it is crisp and golden on both sides. Alternatively, bake it in the oven until crisp. Rub the garlic cloves over the bread and then pour the olive oil over the top. Sprinkle with a little salt and ground black pepper.

Note: Italian-style ciabatta bread, which is available in most supermarkets is best for making bruschetta.

Variation: You can smear the bruschetta with the pulp of a cut tomato, and pop back under the grill for 1-2 minutes.

Crostini di Pane

Bread croûtons

4 thick slices white bread
olive oil for shallow frying

Remove the crusts from the bread and cut it into large dice. Heat the olive oil to a depth of 1.25cm/½ inch in a large frying pan until it is sizzling hot. Add the bread and fry quickly, turning occasionally, until the dice are crisp and golden all over. Remove with a slotted spoon and drain on absorbent kitchen paper. Serve as a garnish for soup.

Salsa Balsamella

White sauce

50g/2oz butter
50g/2oz flour
600ml/1 pint milk
salt and pepper
freshly grated nutmeg

Melt the butter in a saucepan over low heat and stir in the flour until the mixture forms a roux (paste). Cook, stirring constantly, for 2 minutes. Do not allow the roux to brown. Remove the saucepan from the heat and gradually beat in the milk, a little at a time, until all the milk has been incorporated and the sauce is smooth. Return to the heat and bring to the boil, stirring all the time. Reduce the heat immediately and cook over low heat for 10-15 minutes. Season with salt, pepper and nutmeg. Use the sauce in pasta dishes such as lasagne and cannelloni.

Salsa Verde

Green sauce

8 tablespoons olive oil
1 tablespoon lemon juice
2 tablespoons chopped fresh parsley
2 tablespoons finely chopped capers
1 garlic clove, crushed
4 anchovy fillets, mashed
salt and freshly ground black pepper

Mix the olive oil and lemon juice together, and then stir in the remaining ingredients to make a thick vinaigrette. Store in an airtight covered container in the refrigerator for up to 1 week. Serve with grilled fish.

Bagna Cauda

Garlic and anchovy dip

1 x 50g/2oz can anchovies
50g/2oz butter
4 tablespoons olive oil
3 garlic cloves, crushed
4 tablespoons double cream(optional)

To serve:

raw vegetables, e.g. carrot and celery sticks, sliced peppers and fennel bulbs

Drain the anchovies and chop them finely. Heat the butter and oil in a small saucepan and add the garlic and anchovies. Simmer over low heat for 10 minutes. Remove from the heat and set aside to cool slightly. Stir in the cream (if using) and serve warm as a dip with crudités (raw vegetables). Ideally, the pot of bagna cauda should be placed in the centre of the table over a nightlight or table heater, and people dip in and help themselves. This quantity serves 4-6.

INDEX

This book belongs to

....

....

First published by Parragon in 2009
Parragon
Queen Street House
4 Queen Street
Bath BA1 1HE, UK

ISBN 978-1-4075-6021-2

Printed in China

Contents

43
43
43
95
TWIN H
PISTON
CUP

Disney • PIXAR
THE WORLD OF
Cars

Starring

LIGHTNING McQUEEN

SALLY

MATER

CHICK HICKS

DOC

Disney • PIXAR
THE WORLD OF
Cars

"Pit stop! Pit stop!" cried Guido as he zoomed over and joined the gang at Flo's café.

The little forklift buzzed with excitement. Would his friend Lightning McQueen win the Piston Cup?

Earlier that week, Lightning had accidentally found himself in Radiator Springs on his way to the tie-breaker race in California. He had to work hard in Radiator Springs, but he also made lots of friends. Now, everyone in Radiator Springs was sad that Lightning was gone . . . but also excited about his big race.

"Do you think he can beat Chick Hicks?" wondered Sally. "I hear Chick is one mean racecar."

"Lightning can beat anybody, I know it!" said Mater. Lightning and Mater had become best friends in a very short time.

Mater believed in Lightning,
one hundred percent!

htB
CUP

They watched a car with a bright green paint job fill the TV screen. It was Lightning McQueen's rival, Chick Hicks!

"Lightning? Why should I worry about him?" Chick's voice came through the TV speaker. "He ended up in some rusty little town, playing with tractors and taking Sunday drives. He's not serious about winning. But I am!"

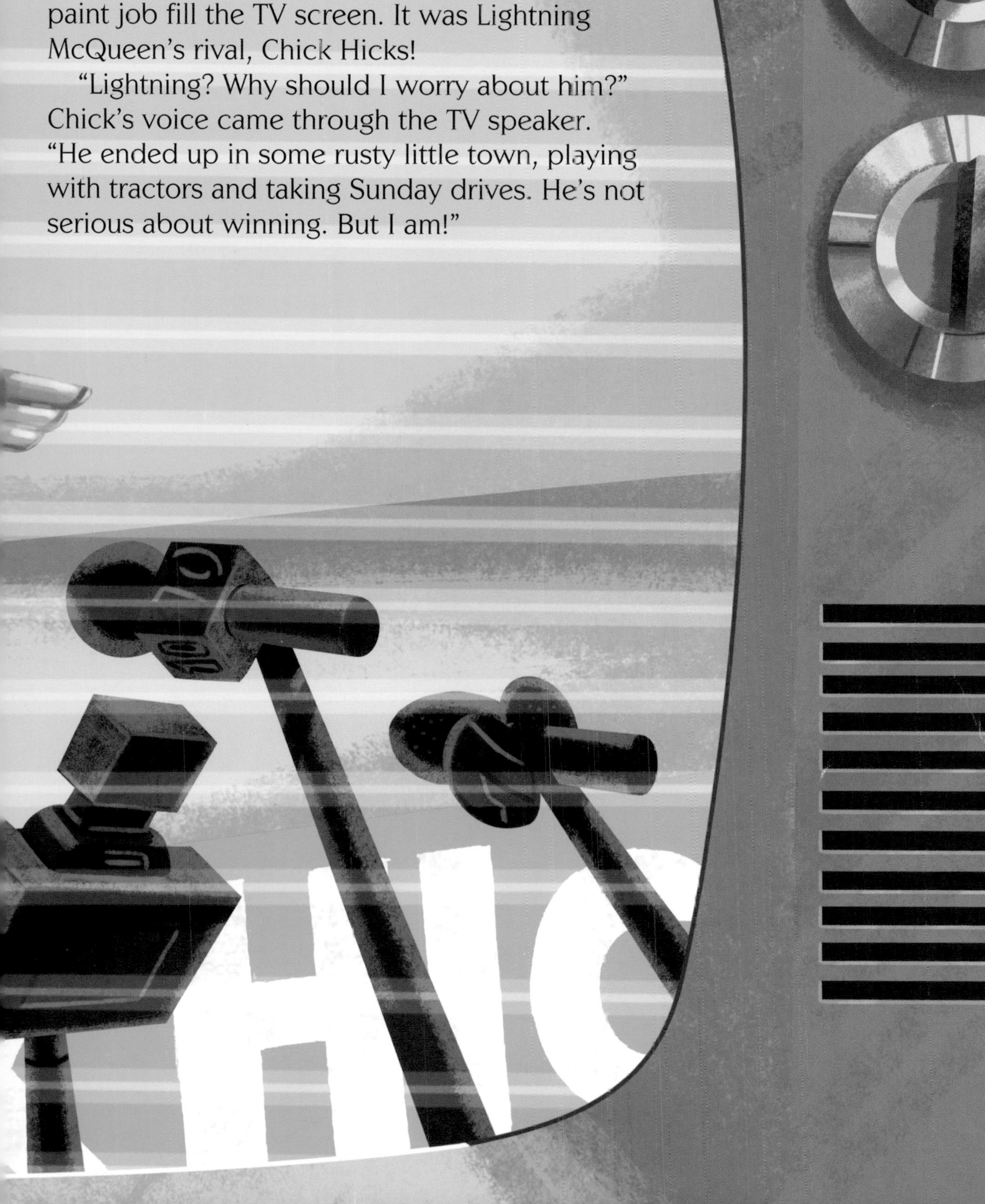

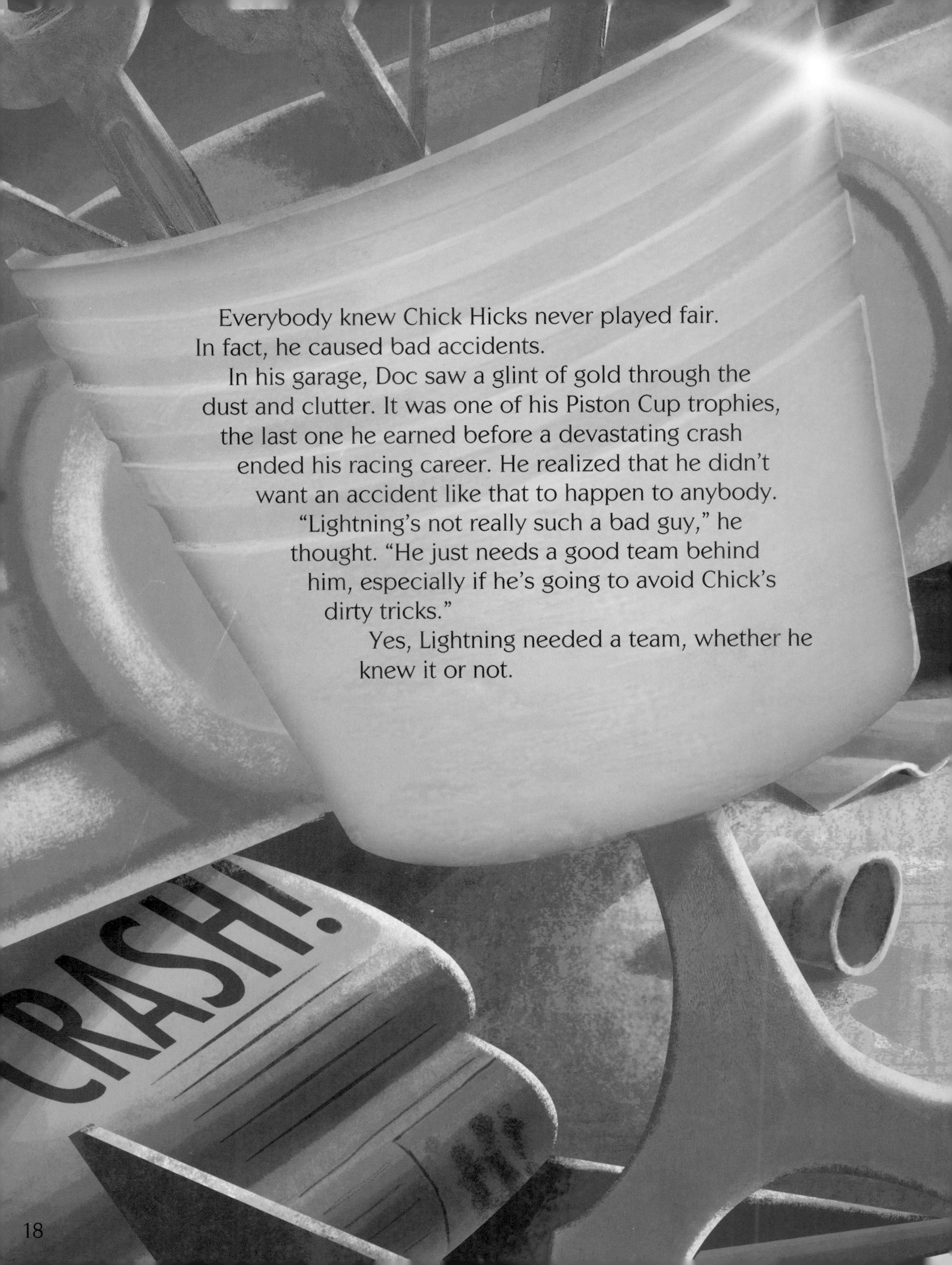

Everybody knew Chick Hicks never played fair. In fact, he caused bad accidents.

In his garage, Doc saw a glint of gold through the dust and clutter. It was one of his Piston Cup trophies, the last one he earned before a devastating crash ended his racing career. He realized that he didn't want an accident like that to happen to anybody.

"Lightning's not really such a bad guy," he thought. "He just needs a good team behind him, especially if he's going to avoid Chick's dirty tricks."

Yes, Lightning needed a team, whether he knew it or not.

"Listen up, everybody," Doc's voice boomed down the main street from Flo's all the way to Sally's motel. "The rookie needs our help. He's out there with no pit crew and two tough opponents. I'm not going to let Lightning McQueen lose just because he thinks he can do it all on his own. Who's with me?"

Everybody was, of course!

Luigi and Guido got to work choosing some tyres. Lightning McQueen would need some good ones.

By morning the crew was inside the stadium. What a feeling it was, to be surrounded by all that excitement! But the Radiator Springs crew had a job to do.

"Pit stop!" said Guido when he saw all the pitties and their tool racks. As soon as Mater unhooked him, he rolled over to a spot to set up.

Sarge took command when he saw the orderly layout of the pit lane and the precise actions of the racing teams.

"You, Flo, over here," he ordered. "Guido, we need the tyres right there."

Ramone had something else in mind, "Hey, Doc! Let me give you a paint job. You gotta let these folks know that you're an important car".

"Not me," said Doc. "Try snazzing-up this pit instead. We need to show off our star car, not me."

Doc drove over to the other side of the track to check out the other crews. But as he neared Chick Hicks' tent he overheard something bad – really bad.

"I'm not gonna let anyone get in the way of me winning that race today," Chick said to his crew. "If I have to, I'll make The King and that rookie wipe out so fast their tyres won't even spin."

Doc peeked in and saw Chick turn and wink to his crew. "The Cup is mine, boys," said Chick.

Doc felt his oil heat up. He couldn't stand for this! It was time to help Lightning, even if it took his last drop of fuel. Could he find Lightning in time to warn him about Chick's evil plans? Doc returned so fast to the group that he almost overheated.

"This is what friendship is all about," thought Doc as Ramone finished painting him. "We are all a family."

And then, as a high-octane boost rushed through him, he climbed the crew-chief platform – with Ramone's blazing letters freshly painted on his side: Number 51, The Fabulous Hudson Hornet.

51
FABULOUS HUDSON
HORNET

"Look, it's the Hudson Hornet!" cried a car in the stands.

The crowd roared and cheered, louder and louder. Everywhere, Doc saw a sea of flashing headlights and flying antenna balls. They were cheering for him!

Doc was too focused on the upcoming race to smile. But it was clear – Doc Hudson was proud to be back, and it felt good to hear the crowds roaring their approval.

43
95
TWIN H
PISTON
CUP

It was all so exciting that no one in the crowd really cared when Chick Hicks was announced the winner of the tiebreaker race.

Instead, they cheered for Lightning as he helped The King cross the finish line. They cheered as they watched Lightning cruise on over to his crew chief, Doc, the Hudson Hornet.

Yes, indeed, the crowd cheered for the real winners of this race: Lightning McQueen and his Radiator Springs family.

Back in Radiator Springs, everybody gathered at Flo's to hear about the race.

"Doc and I want to build a racing headquarters near the town," Lightning told Sally.

Doc nodded. "It will be a special design – a first-class track that won't spoil our beautiful desert landscape."

"A great idea," said Sally. "And it will put Radiator Springs back on the map."

Rust-eze

It wasn't long before Radiator Springs became an international racing sensation. Doc and Lightning sent invitations to race cars all over the world. They came to the town to share tips and techniques on how to become better racers.

THE END

Disney
fairies
TinkerBell

TINKER BELL

STARRING

VIDIA

IRIDESSA

ROSETTA

QUEEN CLARION

Disney
fairies
TinkerBell

One winter's day in London, a baby laughed for the very first time. That laugh floated up and away to meet its destiny. It would become a fairy, just like all first laughs.

It flew straight for the Second Star to the Right, and passed through it in a burst of light. On the other side was . . . Never Land!

The laugh floated towards a magical place in the heart of the island. This was Pixie Hollow, home of the fairies!

Vidia, the fastest flying fairy of them all, guided the arrival into the Pixie Dust Tree. There, a dust-keeper named Terence sprinkled it with pixie dust, and it took the shape of a tiny, adorable fairy.

Clarion, queen of the fairies, helped the newcomer unfurl her two gossamer wings. The new fairy flapped her wings and realized she could fly!

Queen Clarion waved her hand, and several toadstools sprung up around the Pixie Dust Well. Fairies immediately fluttered forwards to place different objects on the pedestals. Rosetta, a garden fairy, brought a flower. Silvermist, a water fairy, carried a droplet of water. Iridessa, a light fairy, placed a lamp on her pedestal.

"They will help you find your talent," the queen explained to the new fairy.

The youngster timidly placed her hand on a beautiful flower. Its glow instantly faded. She reached for a water droplet, but that, too, faded.

The fairy moved on without touching anything else – she was afraid to fail again – but then something amazing happened. As she passed by a hammer, it began to glow. Then it rose up off its pedestal and flew straight for her!

"I've never seen one glow that much before," said Silvermist.

"I do believe you're right," agreed Rosetta. "Li'l daisy-top might be a very rare talent indeed!"

Vidia glowered. She had one of the strongest and rarest talents in Pixie Hollow, and she wasn't looking for competition.

"Tinker fairies," called the queen. "Welcome the newest member of your talent guild – Tinker Bell!"

A large fairy named Clank and a bespectacled fairy named Bobble came forwards to greet Tink. Then they whisked her off for a flying tour of Pixie Hollow. It was almost time for the changing of the seasons, and they could see everyone getting ready.

Finally, the trio landed at Tinkers' Nook. Tink looked around and saw fairies fixing and fashioning all kinds of amazing, useful objects.

Next Clank and Bobble took Tinker Bell to her own little house, which had a closet filled with clothes. The garments turned out to be much too big, but Tink knew just how to fix them.

Tinker Bell put on her new dress and tied her hair up. Then she reported to the workshop. Clank and Bobble couldn't wait to show her all the handy things that tinker fairies made.

Soon Fairy Mary – the no-nonsense fairy who ran Tinkers' Nook – arrived. She noticed the new fairy's dainty hands. "Don't worry, dear, we'll build up those tinker muscles in no time," she exclaimed.

Then, after reminding Clank and Bobble to make their deliveries, she was gone.

A little while later, Tink, Clank and Bobble were on their way. Luckily they had Cheese the mouse – and Clank – to pull the loaded wagon.

PITTER-PATTER! PITTER-PATTER!

The friends heard a sound behind them.

"Sprinting Thistles! Aaaaagh!" screamed Clank. The weeds nearby had come to life and were headed straight for them! The wagon pitched this way and that. Then it lurched down the path and landed in a flowerbed in Springtime Square.

Rosetta, Silvermist, Iridessa and Fawn rushed over to help their friends. The tinkers were unhurt, and soon ready to go back to their deliveries. There were rainbow tubes for Iridessa, milkweed-pod satchels for Fawn and pussy-willow brushes for Rosetta.

Iridessa explained that she would roll up rainbows, put them in the tubes, and take them to the mainland.

"What's the mainland?" Tink asked.

"It's where we're going to go for spring, to change the seasons," replied Silvermist.

Next the tinkers stopped at the Flower Meadow, where Vidia was vacuuming the pollen out of flowers with her whirlwind.

Tinker Bell startled Vidia, and the just-filled pots fell over.

"Hi! What's your talent?" Tink asked.

"I am a fast-flying fairy. Fairies of every talent depend on me," answered Vidia. She made it clear that she didn't think much of tinker fairies.

Tink was insulted. "When I go to the mainland, I'll prove just how important we are!" she replied.

Tink flew off, grumbling to herself. Soon, however, something down on the beach caught her attention. When she landed, she discovered several wonderful treasures buried in the sand.

"Lost Things," said Clank when Tink brought her finds to the Tinkers' Nook workshop.

"They wash up on Never Land from time to time," explained Bobble.

Fairy Mary whisked the trinkets away. The queen's review of the springtime preparations was that night, and there was a lot to do.

Tink decided this was her chance to prove to Vidia just how important a tinker's talent really was!

That evening, the Minister of Spring welcomed Queen Clarion to the review ceremony.

"I think you'll find we have things well in hand," he said proudly. "When the Everblossom blooms, we will be ready to bring spring to the mainland."

Suddenly, Tinker Bell interrupted the proceedings. "I came up with some fantastic things for tinkers to use when we go to the mainland!" she told the queen excitedly.

Tink pulled a homemade paint sprayer out of the wagon and demonstrated it on a flower that needed coloring. But instead of spraying paint, it exploded.

"Has no one explained?" Queen Clarion said gently. "Tinker fairies don't go to the mainland. All of those things are done by the nature-talent fairies. I'm sorry."

The next morning, Tink asked her friends to teach her how to be a nature fairy. She really wanted to go to the mainland. Reluctantly, the other fairies agreed to help. No fairy had ever changed his or her talent before!

Tink's first lesson was on how to become a water fairy. Silvermist showed her how to place a dewdrop on a spider's web, but each time Tink tried, the dewdrop burst.

The light-fairy lesson didn't go any better. Tink lost control of the light and attracted a group of fireflies. They thought Tink's glow was irresistible!

Fawn had Tink's animal fairy lesson all planned. "We're teaching baby birds how to fly," she announced.

Fawn went to a nest, smiled at a bird, and gently encouraged it until the fluffy little creature was flying along right behind her.

Unfortunately, Tink's baby bird seemed terrified. When she nudged it towards the edge of the nest, it even tried to fight her!

"If I end up making acorn kettles the rest of my life, I am holding you personally responsible," Tinker Bell said impatiently.

Tink looked up and saw a majestic bird soaring in the sky. She decided she would ask it to help her teach the baby bird.

Suddenly an ear-splitting screech filled the forest. The bird was a hawk!

Tink hurtled down into the knothole of a tree – but Vidia was already hiding there. Soon the hawk discovered them both, so they jumped down a tunnel inside the tree. When Vidia reached the end of the chute, she could see the hawk outside. She stopped in the nick of time – but Tink accidentally slammed into her and sent Vidia shooting out of the tree. The hawk opened its beak, ready to strike. Luckily, the other fairies were able to chase the bird off.

Vidia was furious. Tink felt awful.

A little while later, Tinker Bell sat on the beach. "Great," she muttered. "At this rate, I should get to the mainland right about, oh, never!"

She angrily threw a pebble and heard a CLUNK! Tink went to investigate and found a broken porcelain box.

By the time her friends found her, Tinker Bell was busily putting her discovery back together. The final touch was a lovely porcelain ballerina that fit into the lid. Tinker Bell gave the dancer a spin, and to her delight, the box played music!

"Do you even realize what you're doing?" asked Rosetta. "Fixing stuff like this – that's what tinkering is!"

"Who cares about going to the mainland anyway?" Silvermist added.

Tink realized her friends didn't want her to change talents. Desperate, she went to visit the only fairy she thought might be able to help.

But Vidia was not in the mood for visitors – especially Tinker Bell.

"You're my last hope," pleaded Tink. "Rosetta won't even try to teach me to be a garden fairy now."

That gave Vidia an idea. She suggested that Tinker Bell prove she was a garden fairy by capturing the Sprinting Thistles.

Tink knew this was her last chance to get to go to the mainland. She built a corral and made a lasso. She rode Cheese into Needlepoint Meadow and used twigs to herd a pair of Thistles into the corral.

"It's working!" Tink cried joyfully. But as she headed back out into the meadow, Vidia quietly blew open the corral gate. The two Thistles ran right out.

Soon other Thistles joined the two that had escaped. It was a stampede!

"Wait! Come back!" yelled Tinker Bell, riding after them.

The Thistles headed to Springtime Square, where they trampled over the carefully organized springtime supplies.

Just then, Queen Clarion appeared. A look of shock crossed her face. "By the Second Star . . . all the preparations for spring – !"

"I'm sorry," Tink whispered as she took to the sky.

Tink decided to leave Pixie Hollow forever, but she couldn't go without one last visit to the workshop. She had to admit that she did love to tinker.

At the workshop, she noticed Cheese sniffing around something at the back of the room – it was trinkets Fairy Mary had taken from her on her first day in Pixie Hollow.

"Lost Things . . . that's it!" she cried as she took them over to her worktable. Tink thought she had an idea that would fix everything.

That night, Queen Clarion gathered all the fairies and explained that spring would not come that year. There simply wasn't enough time to replace all the supplies that had been ruined.

"Wait!" Tinker Bell cried. "I know how we can fix everything!" The clever fairy had designed speedy machines to fix what the Thistles had trampled. She had even used Lost Things to repair her paint sprayer.

Vidia was furious. "Corral the Thistles . . ." she muttered, "I should have told you to go after the hawk!"

Queen Clarion heard this, and looked sharply at Vidia. "I think your fast-flying talent is well-suited to chasing down each and every one of the Thistles," she said sternly.

Tink showed a group of fairies how to assemble a machine to make berry paint. Next she rigged up a vacuum that could collect huge amounts of seeds at a time.

The fairies worked all night using Tink's machines. Early the next morning, Queen Clarion and the ministers of the seasons flew into the square. Before them were more springtime supplies than they had ever seen!

The sun rose, and the Everblossom opened and gave off a golden glow, signaling that it was time to bring springtime to the world. The fairies cheered.

"You did it, Tinker Bell," congratulated Queen Clarion.

"We all did it," Tink replied.

“Queen Clarion,” said Silvermist. “Can’t Tink come with us to the mainland?”

“It’s okay,” Tink protested. “My work is here.”

Fairy Mary flew over, looking sternly at Tink. “I don’t think so, missy!” she said.

She gave a little whistle, and Clank and Bobble led in the wagon. Tink’s music box was inside, all polished and shiny.

“I’d imagine there’s someone out there who’s missing this. Perhaps a certain tinker fairy has a job to do after all . . . on the mainland,” said Fairy Mary.

The nature fairies and Tink went to London. They spread out over the city to deliver their springtime magic.

Tinker Bell found the home where the music box belonged, and tapped on the windowpane. A little girl named Wendy Darling poked her head out of the window. Tink watched from her hiding place as Wendy's face filled with happiness at the discovery of her long-lost treasure. The girl took a small key from a chain around her neck and turned it in a slot. The music box began to play!

Soon the fairies' work was done and it was time for them all to return to Never Land. Tink couldn't wait to get home – she had lots of tinkering to do!

THE END

Disney · PIXAR
TOY
STORY

SPACE RANGER
LIGHTYEAR

BUZZ
LIGHTYEAR

REX

WOODY

SLINKY

HAMM

Disney · PIXAR
TOY
STORY

Woody the cowboy was Andy's favourite toy. He lived in Andy's bedroom with Slinky Dog, Rex the dinosaur, Mr Potato Head, Hamm the pig, Bo Beep and all the other toys. These toys were special. When no one was around, they came to life!

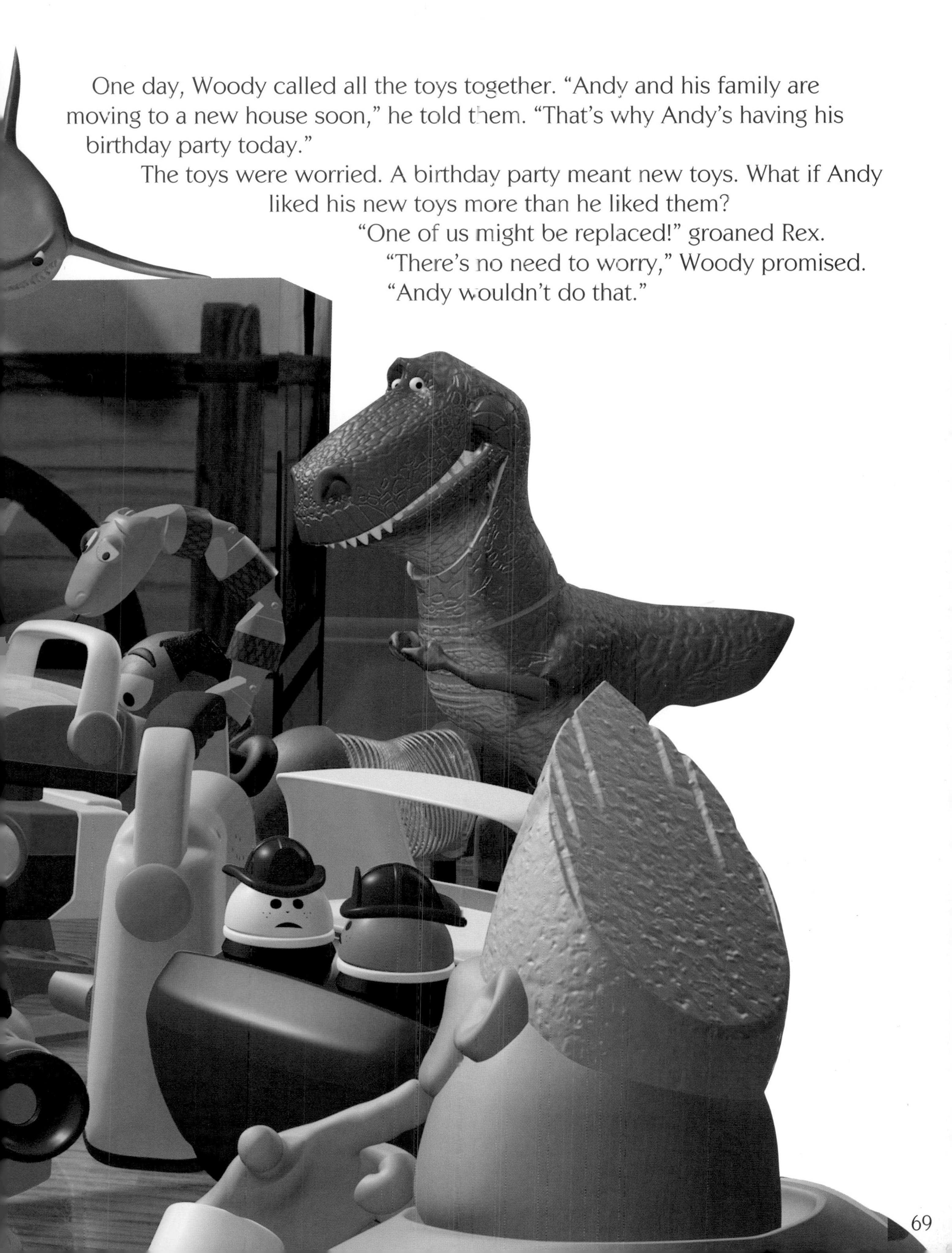

One day, Woody called all the toys together. "Andy and his family are moving to a new house soon," he told them. "That's why Andy's having his birthday party today."

The toys were worried. A birthday party meant new toys. What if Andy liked his new toys more than he liked them?

"One of us might be replaced!" groaned Rex.

"There's no need to worry," Woody promised. "Andy wouldn't do that."

As Andy unwrapped his presents, the toys waited nervously. Everything was all right until the very last parcel – a marvellous spaceman. Andy brought him up to the bedroom and left him there.

"I'm Buzz Lightyear, space ranger," the newcomer said.

Everyone thought Buzz was wonderful. Everyone, that is, except Woody. Woody was jealous!

"You're NOT a space ranger,"he sneered. "You're just a toy like the rest of us!"

Suddenly, they heard barking outside and rushed to the window. Sid, the boy next door, was attacking a toy soldier. His dog, Scud, was watching excitedly.

"Sid's horrible," Rex told Buzz. "He tortures toys just for fun."

The toys watched helplessly as Sid destroyed the soldier.

As the toys went back to their places, Woody was still mad with Buzz. He thought that if he aimed the remote control car at Buzz, the new toy would fall behind the desk and be lost. But the car sped out of control, and everything went wrong – ending up with Buzz falling out of the window. All the toys rushed to the window to see where Buzz had fallen.

"It was an accident!" said Woody. But none of the toys would believe him.

Suddenly, Andy burst into the room. He was going to Pizza Planet and wanted to take a toy.

"I can't find Buzz, Mum," he called. "I'll have to take Woody instead."

But Buzz did go with them! He had fallen into a bush and leapt onto the car just as it drove away.

Pizza Planet was full of arcade games. Buzz thought one was a spaceship and crawled inside, followed by Woody.

It was crammed with toy aliens that were picked up by a claw. Woody and Buzz were horrified when they saw who had managed to grab them – it was Sid, Andy's cruel neighbour.

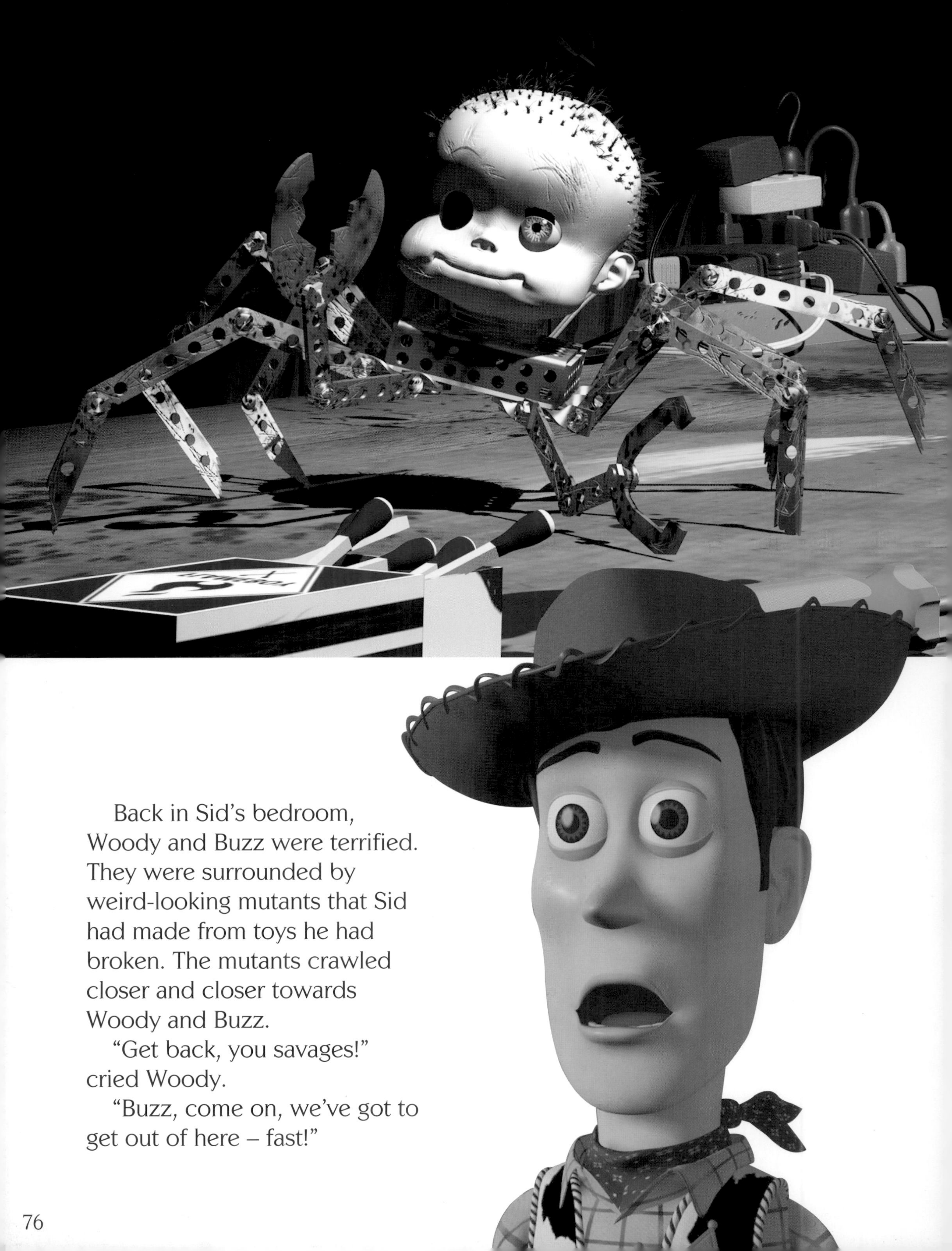

Back in Sid's bedroom, Woody and Buzz were terrified. They were surrounded by weird-looking mutants that Sid had made from toys he had broken. The mutants crawled closer and closer towards Woody and Buzz.

"Get back, you savages!" cried Woody.

"Buzz, come on, we've got to get out of here – fast!"

They had just escaped, when Buzz heard a voice calling:

Buzz left Woody hiding in a cupboard and ran towards the voice. But it was only a television advertisement for the Buzz Lightyear toy. Buzz was stunned. "Is it true?" he whispered. "Am I really… a toy?" Desperate to prove he was a real space ranger, Buzz tried to fly. But he crashed to the floor, breaking his arm.

Woody found Buzz and took him back to Sid's room. Looking out of Sid's window, he saw his old friends in Andy's room.

"Hey guys, help!" Woody called to them, waving madly.

But the toys were angry with Woody because they thought he had hurt Buzz.

Slinky Dog pulled down the blind.

Woody turned sadly away from the window – it seemed that he and Buzz were prisoners in Sid's house.

Luckily, Sid's mutant toys turned out to be friendly after all. That night, they mended Buzz's arm.

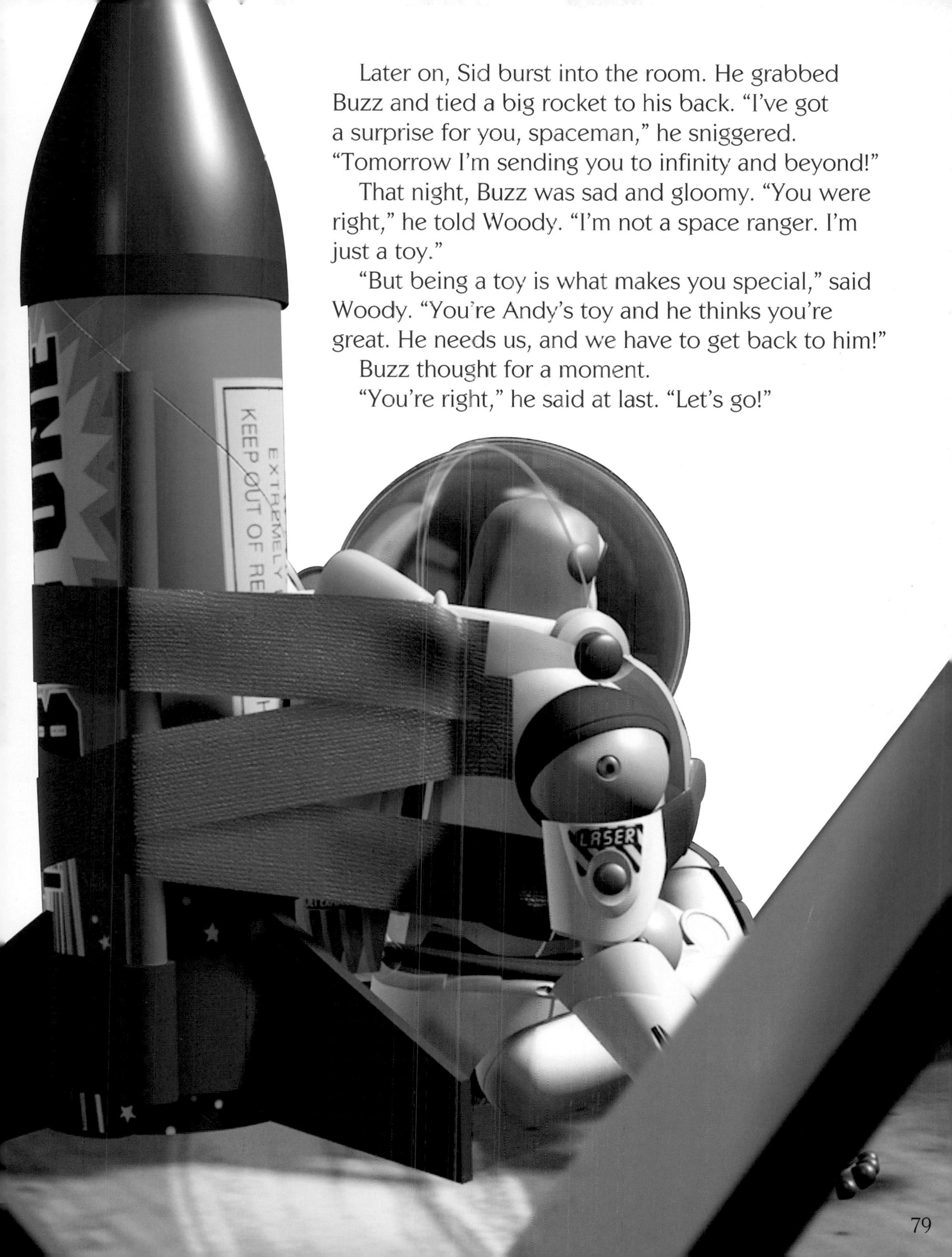

Later on, Sid burst into the room. He grabbed Buzz and tied a big rocket to his back. “I’ve got a surprise for you, spaceman,” he sniggered. “Tomorrow I’m sending you to infinity and beyond!”

That night, Buzz was sad and gloomy. “You were right,” he told Woody. “I’m not a space ranger. I’m just a toy.”

“But being a toy is what makes you special,” said Woody. “You’re Andy’s toy and he thinks you’re great. He needs us, and we have to get back to him!”

Buzz thought for a moment.

“You’re right,” he said at last. “Let’s go!”

But it was too late! **BRRRRRING** rang Sid's alarm clock. Sid reached out, smashed the clock and picked up Buzz.

"Today's the day, spaceman," he said. He rushed downstairs and into the garden, where he started to build a launchpad...

Woody turned to Sid's toys for help.

"Please help me save Buzz," he begged them. "He's my friend." The mutant toys smiled at Woody and nodded. Together, they worked out a plan to rescue Buzz.

Out in the garden, Sid was lighting Buzz's rocket. "Ten! Nine! Eight..." he counted.

10, 9, 8, 7, 6, 5, 4, 3, 2...

Suddenly, Sid spied Woody on the ground. As he picked up the cowboy, his other toys crawled out and surrounded him. Then Woody spoke…

"AAAAAH!" yelled Sid. "Help! These toys are alive!" Screaming, he ran into the house.

Woody and Buzz were free! They thanked the mutant toys for their help and began to make their way home. But Andy's family were just driving away, followed by the removal van!

"It's moving day!" gasped Buzz.

"There they go!" yelled Woody. "Quick! We've got to catch them!"

The two friends rushed after the van. Buzz managed to climb onto the van's back bumper. But Woody was caught by Scud, who had chased them.

"Get away!" shouted Woody, trying to free himself. Scud growled louder...

Bravely, Buzz leapt off the bumper and fought off Scud, who ran back to his house. Now Woody was on the van – but Buzz was stranded on the road!

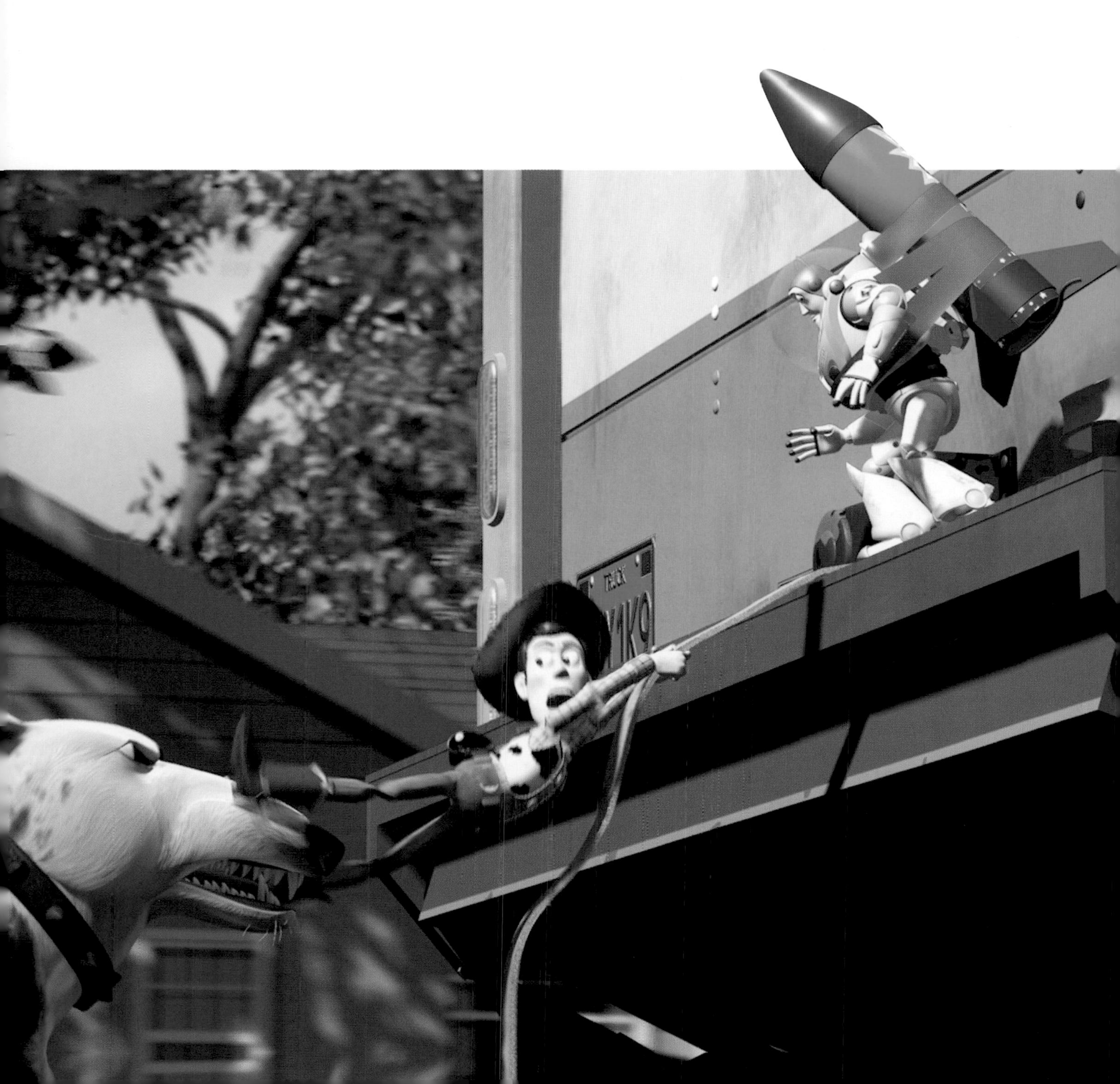

Woody scrambled into the removal van and found the box that contained Andy's toys. They were amazed to see him!

"Buzz is out there and he's in trouble," Woody told them. "We've got to help him!" He grabbed the remote control car and sent it speeding down the street.

The toys thought Woody was trying to get rid of them, just like he had with Buzz!

Shouting angrily, the toys threw Woody out of the van.

But a moment later, the toys' shouts turned to gasps of amazement as they saw Woody and Buzz come zooming towards them in the remote control car.

"Look! They're together!" said Rex. "Woody was telling the truth, after all."

Then, the car slowed down and stopped.

"The **BATTERIES HAVE RUN DOWN!**" howled Buzz.

Woody and Buzz watched miserably as the van disappeared into the distance.

Suddenly, Buzz remembered something. "Woody! The rocket!" he yelled. Sid's rocket was still tied to his back!

They lit the fuse and **WHOOOOSH!** The rocket carried them up into the sky.

Just before it exploded, Buzz pressed a button on his chest. Out popped his wings, freeing them from the rocket.

"We're flying!" laughed Woody, as they soared over the van. Seconds later, they dropped gently through the sunroof of Andy's car.

Woody and Buzz were safe – and they were back with the boy who loved them.

After their adventures, Woody and Buzz became firm friends. Woody no longer felt jealous of Buzz, and the space ranger was happy to be a toy like everyone else. They all settled down together in the new house and the next few months passed happily for everyone.

Christmas came and snow fell thick and soft outside the house. Andy ran downstairs to open his beautifully wrapped Christmas presents.

Once again, the toys watched for the arrival of new toys.

"Nervous, Buzz?" asked Woody.

"No," replied Buzz. "Are you?"

"Tell me, Buzz," laughed Woody. "What could Andy possibly get that would be worse than you?"

The answer came as an excited yelp.

"Oh, no!" laughed the toys –

"A PUPPY!"

THE END

Disney
PRINCESS
Beauty and the Beast

BELLE

THE BEAST

COGSWORTH

STARRING

MRS POTTS
& CHIP

LUMIERE

Disney
PRINCESS
Beauty and the Beast

Once upon a time, a selfish young prince refused to give an old beggar-woman shelter in his castle. But the old woman was really an enchantress. As punishment, she turned the prince into a terrifying beast and cast a spell on everyone in the castle.

Giving the Beast a magic rose she said, "This will bloom until your twenty-first year. If you learn to love another and earn that person's love before the last petal falls, the spell will be broken. If not, you will remain a Beast forever."

In a sleepy village nearby, an eccentric inventor named Maurice lived with his beautiful daughter Belle.

Gaston, a strong and handsome young man from the village, had decided that he wanted to make Belle his wife.

"After all," he told his friend Lefou, "she's the best-looking girl in town. And I deserve the best!"

Gaston arrived at Belle's house, confident that Belle would agree to marry him. But, when he asked her, Belle refused him without a second thought.

She knew she could never marry someone as arrogant and conceited as Gaston!

One day Maurice set off for a fair with his latest invention. As night fell he lost his way and had to seek refuge in the Beast's castle.

Maurice was welcomed by some friendly, enchanted servants, including a candelabra named Lumiere, a clock named Cogsworth, a teapot named Mrs Potts and her son Chip, a teacup.

But the Beast was furious when he discovered a stranger in his home and he threw Maurice into the dungeon. When Maurice's horse returned home alone, Belle set off at once to search for her father.

"Oh, Papa," Belle cried when she found Maurice in the freezing dungeon, "we must get you out of here!"

Sensing danger, Belle turned round. There was the Beast, towering over her and growling loudly.

"Please let my father go," Belle pleaded. "I'll take his place here."

The Beast agreed at once. He dragged Maurice out of the cell and sent him back to the village.

The Beast showed Belle to her room.

"You can go anywhere in the castle," he told her, "except the West Wing. That is forbidden!" Poor Belle was miserable! She missed her father and her home.

The enchanted objects prepared a wonderful meal for her and tried to cheer her up with their singing and dancing.

But Belle was still lonely and later that night she wandered through the castle. She soon found herself in the West Wing. There, among broken furniture and cracked mirrors, she found the magic rose, its petals drooping sadly. Just as Belle reached out to touch the rose, the Beast burst in howling with rage. Terrified, Belle ran out into the snowy night.

Belle leapt on to her father's horse and set off blindly into the dark forest.

Suddenly, she was surrounded by a pack of vicious, hungry wolves.

Just as the wolves closed in for the kill, the Beast appeared through the trees. Fighting bravely, he drove the wolves away.

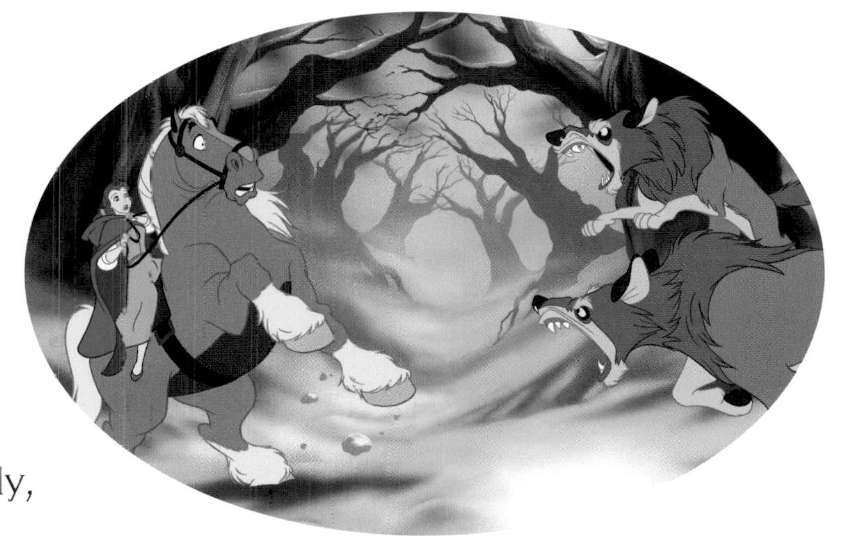

But then the Beast sank to the ground in pain. The wolves had injured him! Belle knew she could not leave him there alone.

She took the Beast back to the castle and gently tended his bleeding wounds. He seemed quite different now and she was no longer frightened of him.

Meanwhile, at the village tavern, Gaston was still brooding over Belle, even though his friends did their best to cheer him up.

Suddenly, the door burst open and Maurice raced in.

"Help!" he cried. "Belle is being held prisoner by a monstrous Beast!"

The men in the tavern burst out laughing. They thought Maurice was mad! But Gaston smiled to himself. He had thought of a way to make Belle marry him! He called a tall, sinister-looking man over to his table and Gaston began to tell him what he had in mind.

As the days passed, Belle and the Beast spent more and more time together. The enchanted servants were delighted. They were certain that Belle would fall in love with their master and break the spell. But time was running out. Each day more petals fell from the magic rose.

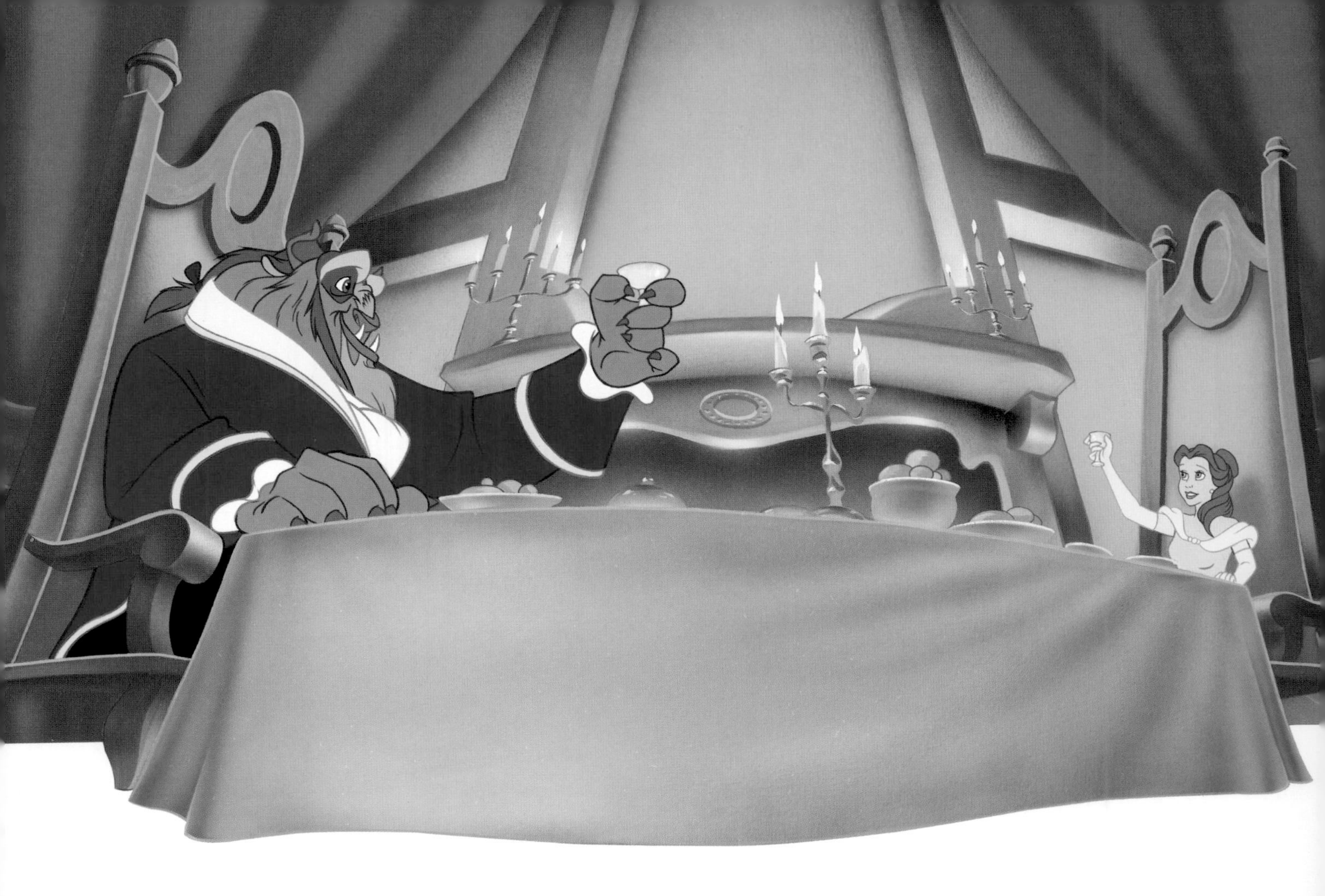

One evening, after dining and dancing together, the Beast and Belle sat out on the terrace in the cool night air.

"Are you happy here, Belle?" asked the Beast.

"Yes," replied Belle. "I just wish I could see my father again."

"You can," said the Beast, and he gave Belle a magic mirror. "This will show you whatever you wish."

"Oh, thank you!" exclaimed Belle. But, as she gazed into it, Belle saw her father lost and trembling with cold as he searched for Belle!

Although the Beast loved Belle, he knew he had to let her go to her father.
"Take the mirror with you," he said sadly, "so you can remember me."
Belle set off from the castle and soon found Maurice. She brought him safely home and put him to bed.

The next day Gaston arrived at Belle's house with a crowd of villagers. He said that Maurice would be taken to an asylum unless Belle agreed to marry him.

"My father's not mad!" cried Belle.

"He must be," said Lefou. "He was raving about a monstrous beast!"

"The Beast is real!" cried Belle. "Look!"

She held up the magic mirror and the crowd saw the Beast for themselves. They all shouted with fear and refused to listen to Belle when she told them the Beast was kind and good.

Furious that his plan had failed, Gaston gathered the mob together to attack the Beast's castle.

The men marched up to the castle doors and broke them down. Cogsworth led the enchanted servants in a brave defence of the castle. But the Beast missed Belle and was too heartbroken to fight, even when Gaston beat him with a club and drove him on to the castle roof.

Only when he heard Belle's voice did the Beast look up.

"You came back!" he cried, rushing to embrace Belle.

This was the chance Gaston had been waiting for.

Drawing his dagger, he stabbed the Beast in the back. But as the Beast collapsed, Gaston tripped – and fell tumbling from the roof.

Belle ran to the wounded Beast and bent to kiss him. The last petal was just about to fall from the rose.

"You can't die," sobbed Belle. "I love you! I wish I had never left you alone!"

Suddenly, a magic mist surrounded the Beast and, before Belle's astonished eyes, he changed into the handsome young prince he had once been.

One by one, the enchanted servants became human again. Weeping with joy, they hugged each other as the Prince swept Belle into his arms.

The Prince had found his true love at last and the spell of the enchantress was broken. As the sun burst through the clouds, they knew they would all live together in happiness for ever after.

THE END

Disney · PIXAR
RATATOUILLE
(rat·a·too·ee)

REMY

EMILE

STARRING

COLETTE

SKINNER

LINGUINI

Disney · PIXAR
RATATOUILLE
(rat·a·too·ee)

Deep in the French countryside, a colony of rats was busy sifting through a compost pile for food.

It was one rat's job to make sure the scraps of food were safe to eat. That rat's name was Remy. Remy had a highly developed sense of taste and smell and was the 'poison checker' for the rest of the rat colony.

Emile, his younger (but bigger) brother, ate anything in sight. He was always impressed by Remy's gift.

Secretly, Remy had much bigger dreams.

He wanted to be a great chef, like his idol, the late, great chef Auguste Gusteau. In fact, Remy had even learned to read Gusteau's cookbook...

Anyone Can Cook!

Both the cookbook and the compost pile belonged to an old woman named Mabel. Her attic was home to the entire rat colony, though she didn't know it.

One day, Remy and Emile sneaked into her kitchen together. Remy always enjoyed looking for spices in her cupboards.

The nervous Emile did not. Their father, Django, always said humans were dangerous and to stay far away from them.

Suddenly, Remy raced from the kitchen to the TV. He saw his idol Gusteau! Remy learned that Gusteau had died from a broken heart when his restaurant lost its five-star status.

Remy was so shocked by the news about Gusteau that he didn't notice Mabel waking up.

He and Emile had to scramble to escape as Mabel chased them. In the chaos, the ceiling cracked and the entire rat colony fell to the floor.

"Evacuate!" Django shouted to the rats.

As the other rats headed out the door, Remy went back into the kitchen for the cookbook. He couldn't leave it behind.

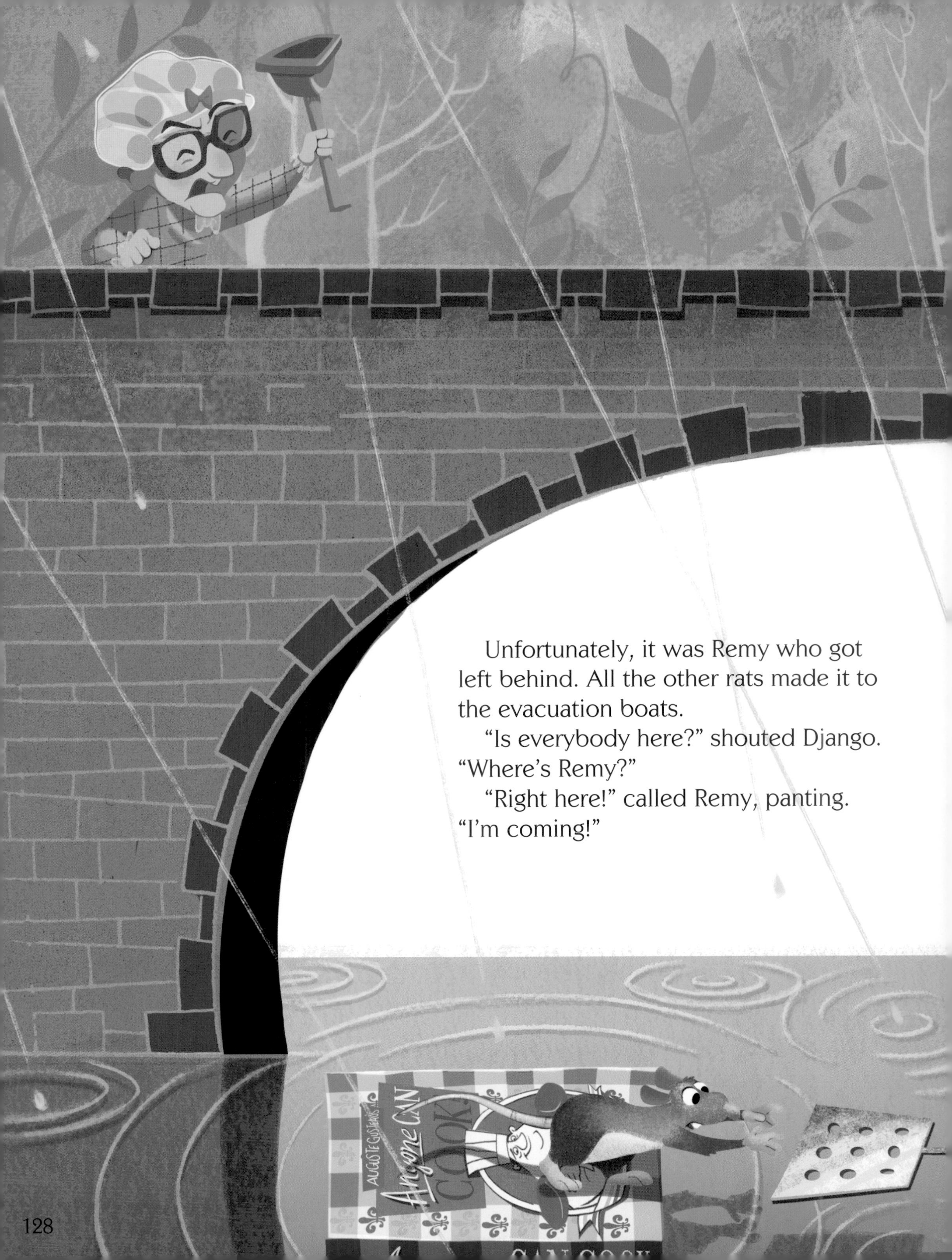

Unfortunately, it was Remy who got left behind. All the other rats made it to the evacuation boats.

"Is everybody here?" shouted Django. "Where's Remy?"

"Right here!" called Remy, panting. "I'm coming!"

Remy threw the cookbook into the water and hopped on board.

"Come on, son!" called Django. "You can make it!"

Poor Remy didn't make it. Separated from his family, the little rat swept down the sewer currents. Hungry, sad and wet, he finally found a landing place, and started drying out the pages of his cookbook. Suddenly, Gusteau seemed to come to life on a page in the cookbook. "If you are hungry, go up and look around," said Gusteau. "If you focus on what you've left behind, you will never be able to see what lies ahead."

So Remy climbed up and up until he saw…

"Paris?" he said breathlessly, taking in the view. "All this time I've been underneath Paris? Wow! It's beautiful!"

"The most beautiful," said Gusteau with a sigh.

Remy looked to his left. His jaw dropped. The sign for Gusteau's restaurant was right nearby.

"Your restaurant?" Remy said to Gusteau. "You've led me to your restaurant!"

To Remy, this was a dream come true.

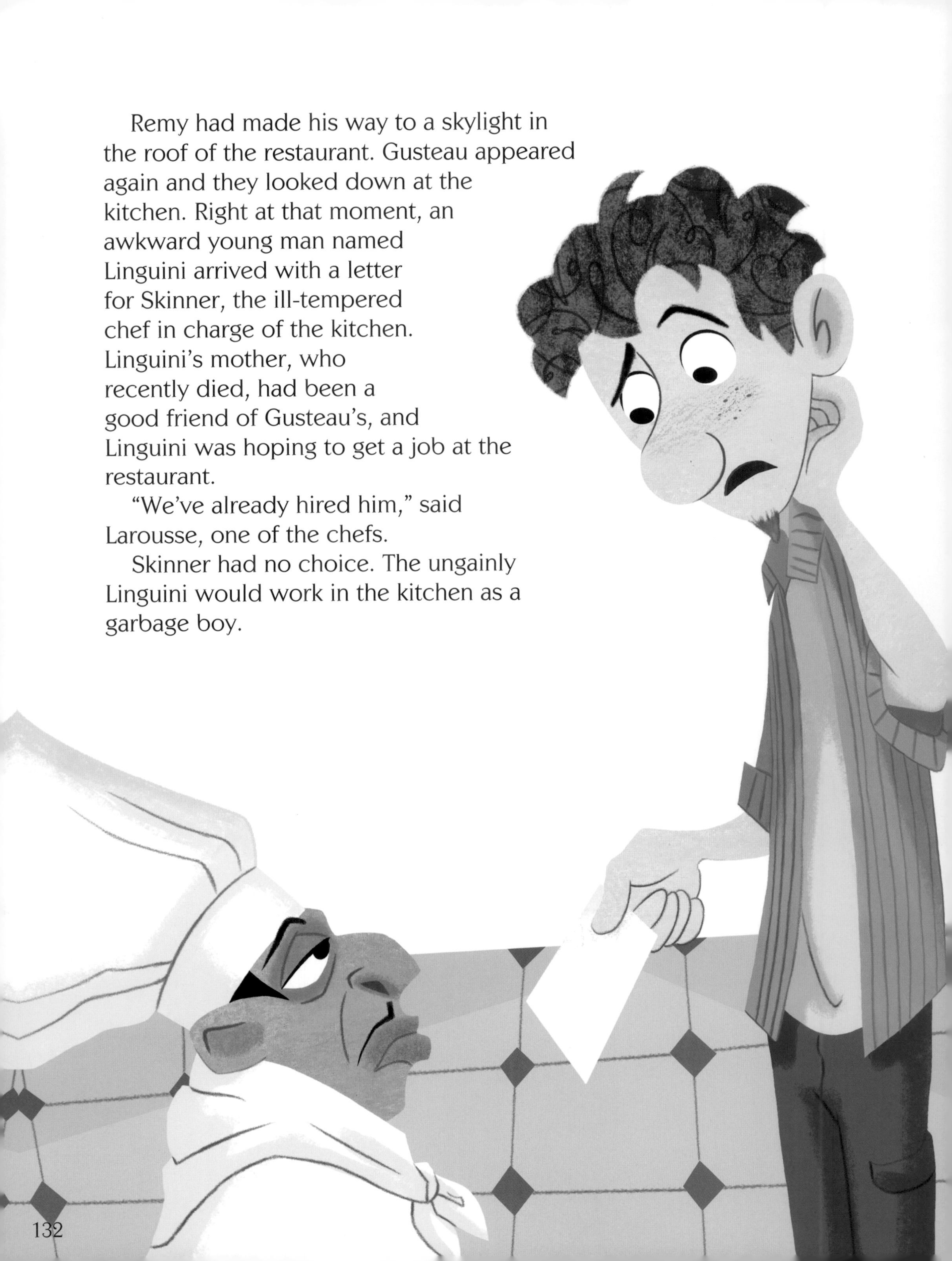

Remy had made his way to a skylight in the roof of the restaurant. Gusteau appeared again and they looked down at the kitchen. Right at that moment, an awkward young man named Linguini arrived with a letter for Skinner, the ill-tempered chef in charge of the kitchen. Linguini's mother, who recently died, had been a good friend of Gusteau's, and Linguini was hoping to get a job at the restaurant.

"We've already hired him," said Larousse, one of the chefs.

Skinner had no choice. The ungainly Linguini would work in the kitchen as a garbage boy.

Linguini went right to work, but he was very clumsy. Remy watched in horror from the skylight as Linguini accidentally spilled a pot of soup and secretly began adding ingredients to try and fix it.

"Do something!" Remy shouted to the figure of Gusteau.

"He's ruining the soup!"

Gusteau shrugged. "What can I do? I'm a figment of your imagination."

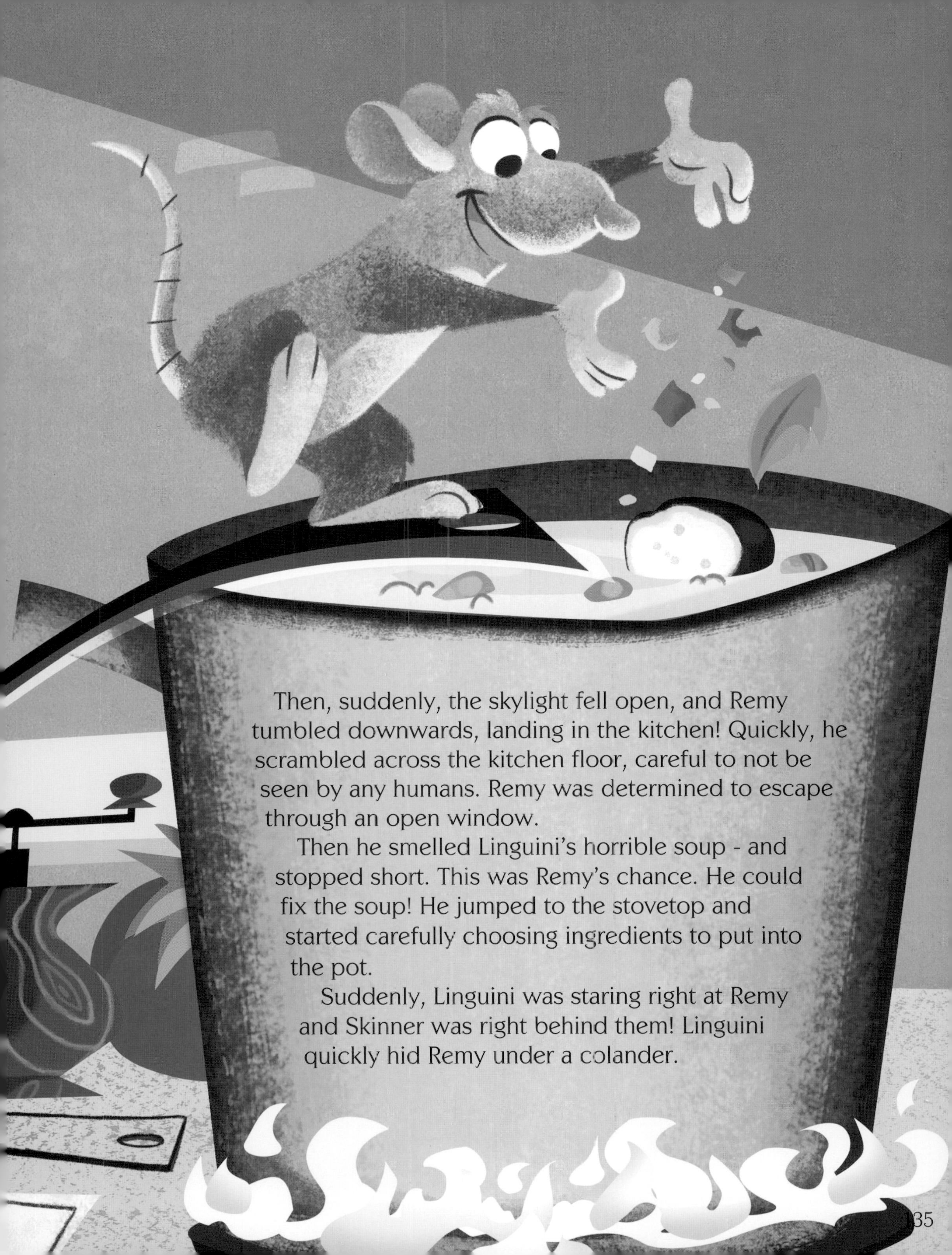

Then, suddenly, the skylight fell open, and Remy tumbled downwards, landing in the kitchen! Quickly, he scrambled across the kitchen floor, careful to not be seen by any humans. Remy was determined to escape through an open window.

Then he smelled Linguini's horrible soup - and stopped short. This was Remy's chance. He could fix the soup! He jumped to the stovetop and started carefully choosing ingredients to put into the pot.

Suddenly, Linguini was staring right at Remy and Skinner was right behind them! Linguini quickly hid Remy under a colander.

"How dare you cook in my kitchen!" shouted Skinner, who had spotted Linguini holding a ladle. He fired Linguini on the spot.

But worse things were happening. While Skinner was yelling the waiter whisked a bowl of the soup off to the dining room to an important food critic.

As the chefs waited nervously in the kitchen, word came back from the waiter. The soup was delicious! The critic loved it!

Colette, one of the cooks, looked at Linguini. "You can't fire him!" she said to Skinner. "Wasn't Gusteau's motto that anyone can cook? Linguini should be given a chance to cook in the kitchen. Besides, how would it look if the restaurant fired the person who created the soup that a critic liked?"

Angrily, Skinner gave in, and assigned Colette to teach Linguini in the kitchen.

In the commotion, Remy made a move for the window. But Skinner spotted him. He made Linguini catch the rat in a jar.

"Take it away from here, far way. Dispose of it. Go!"

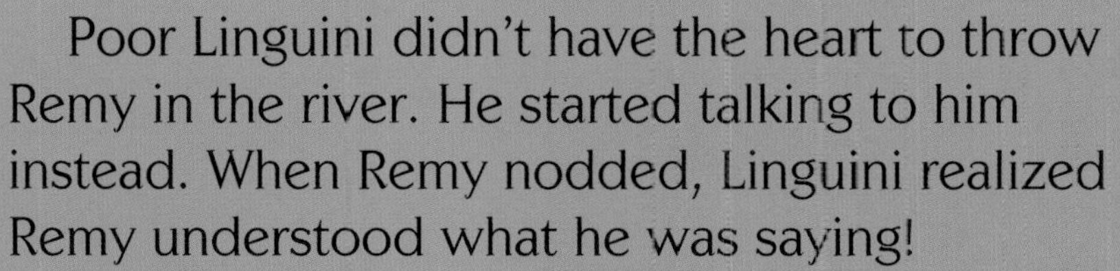

Poor Linguini didn't have the heart to throw Remy in the river. He started talking to him instead. When Remy nodded, Linguini realized Remy understood what he was saying!

"Wait. You can cook, right?" asked Linguini. Linguini made a deal with Remy. Linguini would let Remy out if Remy promised to help him cook. But as soon as Linguini opened the jar, Remy ran away.

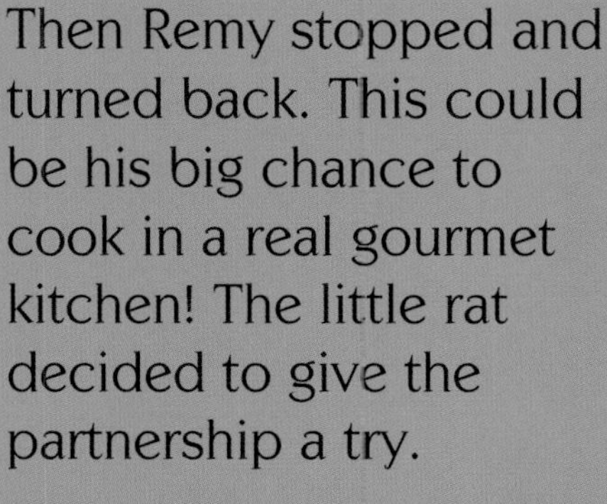

Then Remy stopped and turned back. This could be his big chance to cook in a real gourmet kitchen! The little rat decided to give the partnership a try.

Back in the kitchen, Linguini hid Remy in his shirt and Remy tried to help Linguini with his cooking. Remy tried to guide Linguini by biting and tickling him, but it wasn't working.

Suddenly, Skinner burst through the door and caught a glimpse of Remy. "The rat! I saw it!" shouted the nasty little man.

Linguini quickly hid Remy in his hat and ducked out – almost colliding with a waiter! But Remy tugged Linguini's hair at the last minute and Linguini jerked backwards like a puppet. Could this be their new system?

Linguini and Remy went home to practise cooking. Remy guided Linguini by tugging his hair and before too long, Linguini could even cook blindfolded!

In the meantime, Skinner finally read the letter from Linguini's mother and was now keeping a secret: Auguste Gusteau was Linguini's father. Nobody knew, not even Linguini…or Gusteau!

That meant the restaurant rightfully belonged to Linguini. Skinner was horrified. He had always thought the restaurant would be his! He had to do something to make sure Linguini never found out.

One night, Remy was relaxing in the alley behind the restaurant, enjoying his cooking success, when Emile appeared.

Emile led his long-lost brother to the rat colony's new home. There, in honour of Remy's homecoming, a hopping party filled the sewer with music and dancing.

But soon, Remy said he had to leave. He tried to explain that he had new friends, a job, even a new place to live. In fact…he was living with a human. Django scowled and tried to convince his son that humans were dangerous. But Remy was sure that his situation was different, that Linguini was different. Against his father's wishes, Remy headed back to the restaurant.

Not long afterwards, Remy found the papers in Skinner's office saying that Linguini was the rightful owner of the restaurant.

Suddenly, Skinner appeared! Remy grabbed both the will and the letter, and ran. Skinner chased him. Skinner did not want those papers to get into the wrong hands! Remy held the papers in his mouth, using them almost like wings, to glide onto a boat. The chef ended up in the river.

By the time the soaking-wet Skinner got back to Gusteau's, Linguini was in his office with Colette. Linguini knew the truth now, and he fired Skinner on the spot.

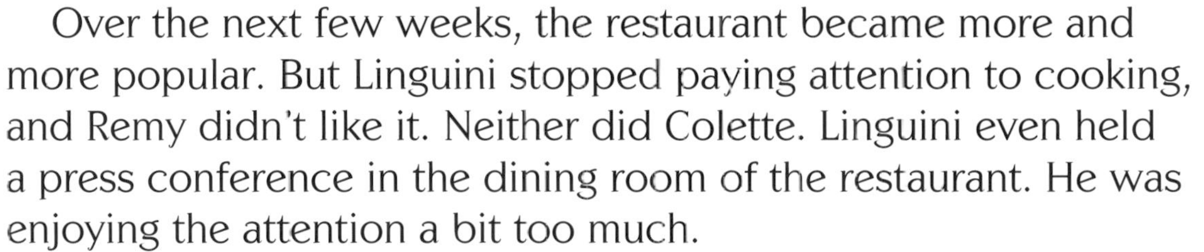

Over the next few weeks, the restaurant became more and more popular. But Linguini stopped paying attention to cooking, and Remy didn't like it. Neither did Colette. Linguini even held a press conference in the dining room of the restaurant. He was enjoying the attention a bit too much.

Suddenly, the famous critic Ego – the very same Ego who had ruined Gusteau's – arrived and gave his warning: "I will return tomorrow night with high expectations."

After Ego's announcement, Colette dragged Linguini back to the kitchen, with Remy in tow. Remy was furious that Linguini wasn't more worried about cooking, and he yanked Linguini's hair, hard.

Linguini got angry. He took Remy out to the back and said, "You take a break, Little Chef. I'm not your puppet."

Remy was cross with Linguini. Later that night, Remy showed the entire rat colony how to get into the walk-in refrigerator and told them to take whatever they wanted.

That's when Linguini returned to apologize.

"You're stealing from me?" Linguini furiously asked Remy. "I thought you were my friend. I trusted you! Get out and don't ever come back!"

But Remy did come back. He felt horrible. Plus, Ego had come to review the restaurant. Remy knew his friend Linguini needed help. Boldly, Remy walked alone through the doors, into the bustling kitchen.

"Rat!" shrieked all the chefs.

"Don't touch him!" shouted Linguini. "The truth is, I have no talent at all. But this rat – he's the cook."

From the shadows, Django watched the human defend Remy!

Still, the cooks walked out – even Colette.

Only Remy and Linguini were left to cook for Anton Ego.

"I was wrong about you. About him," Django told Remy, referring to how Linguini stood up for the little rat. "I'm proud of you."

Django whistled, and rats instantly filled the kitchen. "We're not cooks, but you tell us what to do and we'll get it done."

When the health inspector arrived, Django sent a team of rats to whisk him away. After going through the dishwasher to clean themselves, the other rats began to cook.

Even Colette came back. She was a little shocked to see all the rats, but she soon agreed to help cook the dish Remy had chosen for Ego. It was ratatouille.

Linguini, acting as waiter, served the dish to Ego. The delicious ratatouille brought back a warm, comforting memory from Ego's childhood. When Ego asked to meet the chef, Linguini and Colette waited until all the other customers left the restaurant, then they brought out Remy.

The next morning Ego gave the restaurant a rave review!

Unfortunately, the health inspector closed down Gusteau's, but not all was lost for Remy and his friends. Ego retired and invested in a small but quaint bistro, La Ratatouille. Linguine was the waiter, and Colette cooked - along with one very special, little chef. The restaurant would become well loved by its customers, both big and small.

Remy's dreams had finally come true.

THE END

Disney • PIXAR

WALL•E

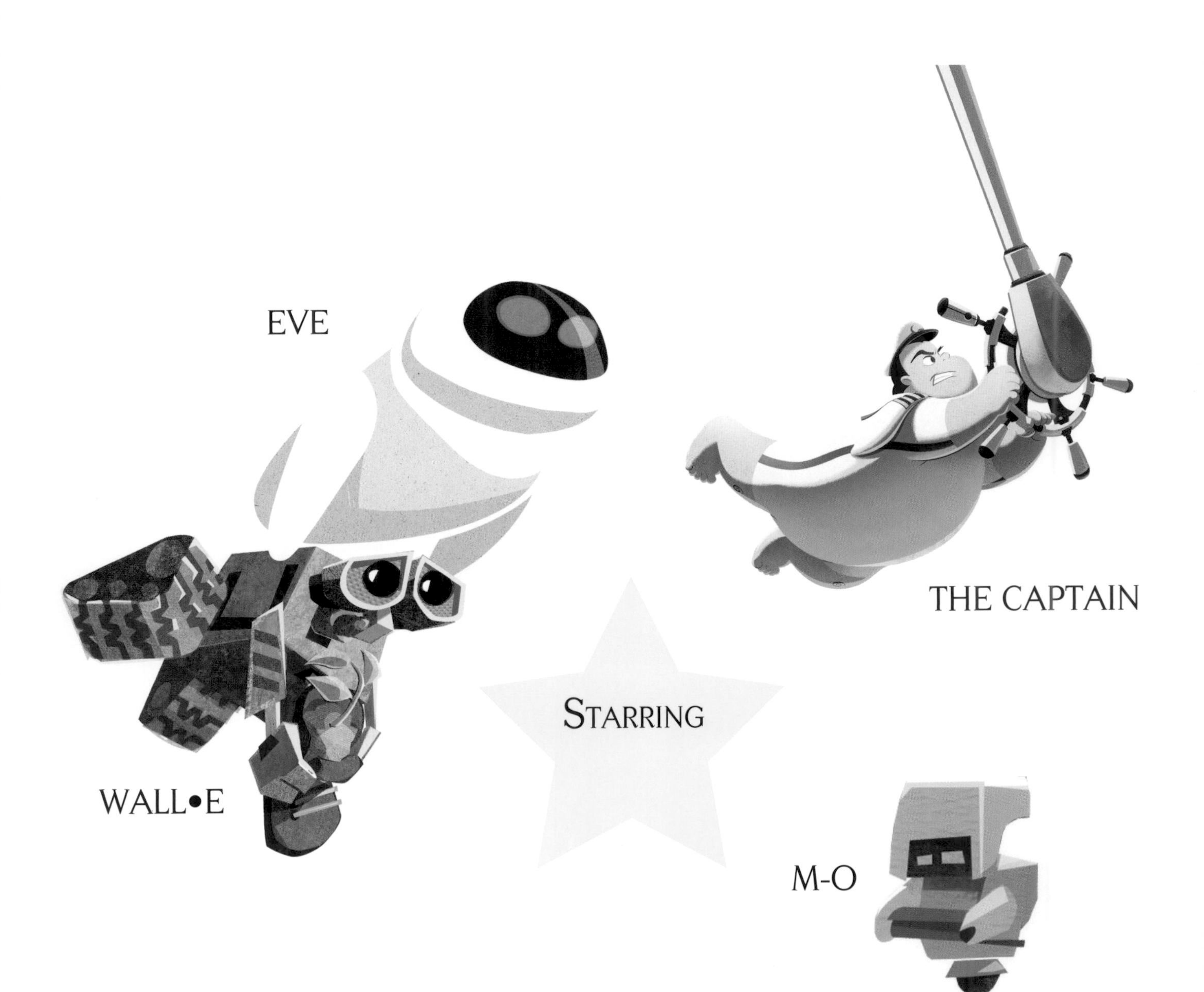
EVE
THE CAPTAIN
STARRING
WALL•E
M-O

Disney · PIXAR

WALL·E

If you lived back in the 29th century, you would live off in space with all the other people from Earth.

Long ago, Earth had been evacuated because it was too polluted. No one could live there until someone cleaned up the planet. And there was someone – just one – left behind to do that work.

WALL•E was a Waste Allocation Load Lifter, Earth-Class. He didn't mind his lonely job of compacting trash. He looked at it as a sort of treasure hunt. He never knew what he would find each day in the trash.

BnL

But WALL•E wanted more in life. He didn't ask for much. He just wanted to hold hands with someone – someone he loved. He had seen this watching his favourite movie over and over. It was his dream.

One day, WALL•E was out compacting and cubing trash when he found something special. It was a plant. His pet cockroach chirped, knowing that his friend would be really interested in this green thing. Neither one of them had ever seen anything like it before. WALL•E took it home.

Soon afterwards, another robot landed on Earth. WALL•E fell in love with the sleek new robot at first sight. Her name was EVE, and over time, WALL•E figured out that she was looking for something. But she wouldn't tell him what it was.

WALL•E took her to his home and showed her all the treasures he had collected from the trash.

But when WALL•E showed her the plant, she grabbed it from him and stored it in a secret compartment in her chest.

Then she shut down. She slept and slept, no matter how hard WALL•E tried to wake her up.

Soon EVE's ship returned to take her away. No! WALL•E loved her. He didn't want her to leave. So he latched onto the outside of her ship and followed her into space.

The spaceship docked inside an enormous ship called the *Axiom*. The Captain's robot assistant, Gopher, wrapped EVE in energy bands and drove her away. WALL•E raced after her. And M-O, a cleaner-bot, chased WALL•E. (M-O was programmed to clean, clean, clean. WALL•E, the little trash-compacting robot from Earth, was his biggest challenge ever.)

As WALL•E chased EVE, he accidentally disabled passenger Mary's electronic system. Mary blinked and looked around.

She saw the world around her, instead of viewing it all digitally over her holo-screen. She liked the change.

Finally EVE was ready to give the plant to the Captain. By doing so, she would prove that Earth was clean enough that a plant could now grow there. That meant everyone could return to the planet.

But EVE's compartment was empty. The plant had disappeared!

Disappointed, the Captain sent EVE to the repair ward, along with WALL•E. When they got there, WALL•E thought some orderlies were hurting EVE. So he helped her escape, along with all the reject-bots from the repair ward.

But there was a problem. Once they ran free, they looked like escaped convicts. A warning broadcast their escape throughout the *Axiom*. The ship's stewards tried to catch them.

To avoid being captured, EVE took WALL•E to an escape pod. She would send him to Earth where he would be safe, and then she could find the plant. Instead, Gopher appeared. He had the plant! He put it in the escape pod. WALL•E and the plant were launched into space – not towards Earth, but far into outer space! WALL•E panicked and pushed a lot of buttons.

WALL•E pushed the wrong button. The pod exploded, but he escaped. EVE went to try to help him. Whoosh! WALL•E zoomed up to EVE . . . and showed her that he had saved the plant. Delighted, she leaned in towards him, and an arc of electricity passed between their foreheads – a robot kiss.

Soon they were floating
in space, dancing and giggling.

Back on the *Axiom,* WALL•E tried to wait as EVE delivered the plant to the Captain. The Captain was so excited that he was ready to return to Earth, but Auto wouldn't let him.

Quickly Gopher snatched the plant and dumped it down the trash chute. It hit WALL•E. The little bot was climbing up to get to EVE. Happily he delivered the plant right to her. But Auto electrocuted WALL•E and sent him back down the chute with EVE.

WALL•E and EVE ended up in the ship's garbage bay. EVE rescued the injured little bot while WALL•E tried to give her the plant. He still thought she wanted it more than anything else. But WALL•E was wrong. EVE just wanted to help WALL•E now. M-O helped, still trying to clean WALL•E.

Soon EVE flew all three of them up and out of the garbage bay, with the plant in hand. She wanted to get WALL•E home to Earth so she could find the right parts to fix him.

The Captain was fighting Auto for control of the ship by now. He sent a message to EVE, telling her to take the plant to a large machine called the holo-detector. It would scan the plant and ready the ship to head towards Earth. That was all EVE cared about now.

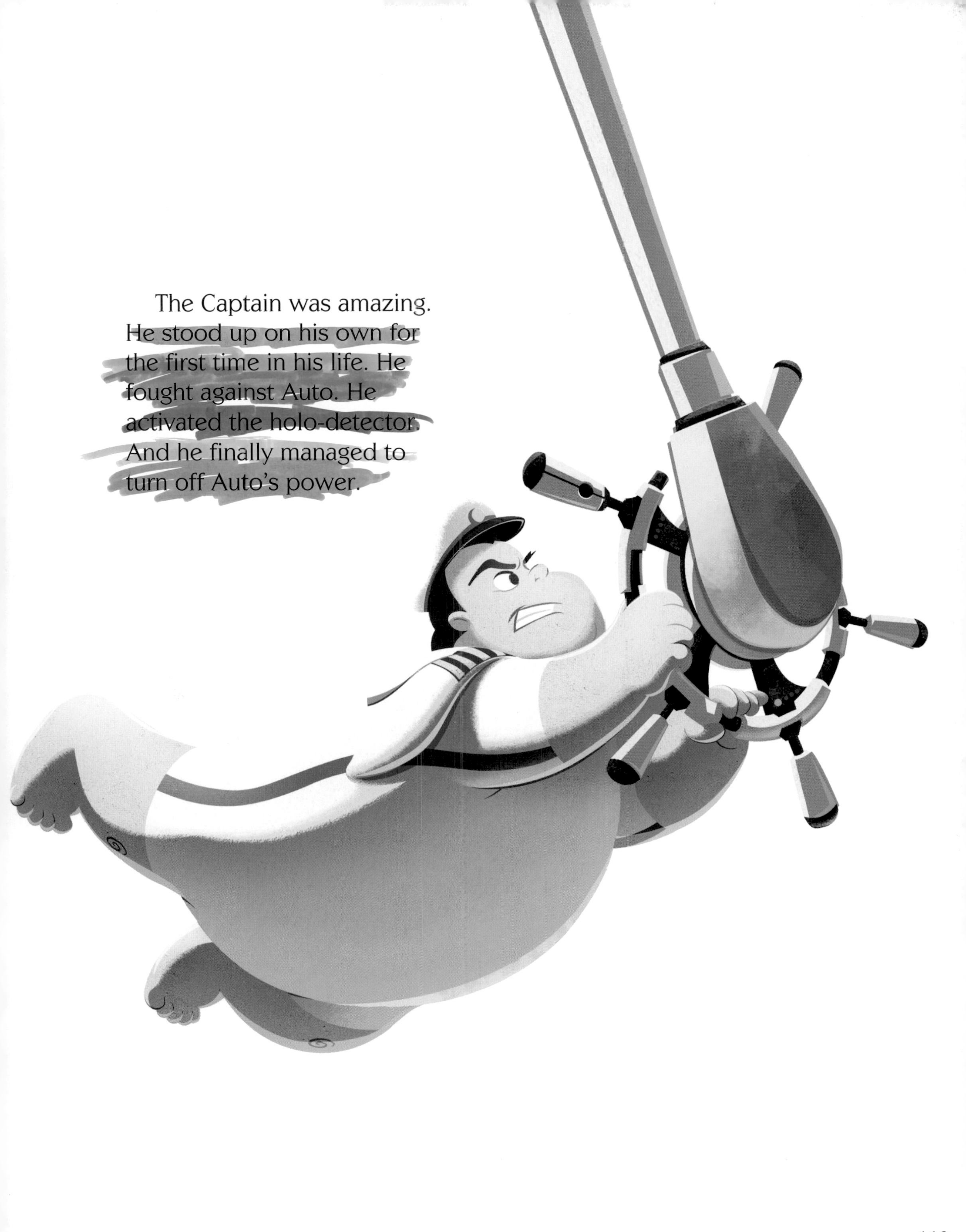

The Captain was amazing. He stood up on his own for the first time in his life. He fought against Auto. He activated the holo-detector. And he finally managed to turn off Auto's power.

EVE fought to reach the holo-detector. At last she put the plant inside the machine. The holo-detector scanned the plant. Finally they could return to Earth.

But not all was well. WALL•E had been crushed by the giant machine, trying to keep it up high enough.

Heartbroken, EVE pulled WALL•E's crushed body from under the holo-detector.

More determined than before, EVE wanted to take him home to his truck where she could find the right parts to bring him back to life.

As soon as the *Axiom* landed on Earth, EVE headed straight for WALL•E's home and began to repair him. At last, he powered up . . . and began cubing trash. Something was wrong. He was just another trash-cubing robot. All the love was gone. He didn't even recognize EVE.

Sadly, EVE held WALL•E's hand and leaned towards him.

An electric arc passed between their heads – the robot kiss. She was saying good-bye.

Then . . . WALL•E's hand began to move. EVE looked into his eyes. He was coming back to life! He recognized her!

"Ee-vah?" he said.

After following EVE across the universe, WALL•E had ended up right where he had started: home. But this time, he had the one thing he had always wanted – EVE's hand clasped in his own.

THE LION KING

PUMBAA

SIMBA

SCAR

TIMON

STARRING

MUFASA

NALA

ZAZU

RAFIKI

THE LION KING

As the morning sun rose high over the African plain, animals and birds gathered at the foot of Pride Rock.

"There he is!" one of them cried suddenly. "There's the new Prince!" Everyone cheered and stamped their feet. "Welcome Prince Simba!" they shouted.

They watched in silence as Rafiki, a wise old baboon, raised the lion cub high in the air. The clouds parted and the sun's rays shone down on the future King. Slowly Rafiki lowered his arms and took Simba back to his proud parents, King Mufasa and Queen Sarabi.

It was a very special day.

Time passed quickly for little Simba. There was so much to learn. One morning the King showed his son round the kingdom. "Remember," Mufasa warned, "a good king must respect all creatures, for we exist together in the great Circle of Life."

Later that day Simba met his uncle, Scar. The cub proudly told him that he had seen the whole of his future kingdom.

"Even beyond the northern border?" Scar asked slyly.

"Well, no," said Simba sadly. "My father has forbidden me to go there."

"Quite right," said Scar. "Only the bravest lions go there. An elephant graveyard is no place for a young prince."

Simba hurried away to find his best friend, a young lioness called Nala. Even though he knew it was wrong, Simba had decided to visit the elephant graveyard with Nala that very day.

He had no idea that Scar had ordered three hyenas to go to the elephant graveyard too. Scar wanted them to kill the cub as the first step in his plan to take over Mufasa's kingdom.

Simba raced ahead across the plains, leading Nala to the forbidden place. Eventually they reached a pile of bones and Simba knew they had arrived.

"It's creepy here." said Nala. "Where are we?"

"This is the elephant graveyard!" Simba cried. He was looking at a skull when he saw Zazu, his father's adviser.

"You must leave here immediately!" Zazu commanded. "You are in great danger."

But it was already too late! They were trapped. Three hyenas had surrounded them, laughing menacingly.

Simba took a deep breath and tried to roar – but only a squeaky rumble came out. The hyenas laughed hysterically.

Simba took another deep breath.

ROAARR! The three hyenas looked round into the eyes of – King Mufasa. The hyenas fled howling into the mist.

Mufasa sent Nala and Zazu ahead and walked slowly home with his son. “Simba, I’m disappointed in you. You disobeyed me and put yourself and others in great danger.”

Simba felt terrible. “I was only trying to be brave like you,” he tried to explain.

“Being brave doesn’t mean you go looking for trouble,” said the King gently.

The moon shone brightly above them and the stars twinkled in the dark sky.

Mufasa stopped. "Look at the stars! From there the great kings of the past look down on us. Just remember that they'll always be there to guide you, and so will I."

Simba nodded. "I'll remember."

By the next day Scar had devised another plan to get rid of Mufasa and Simba. He led Simba to the bottom of a gorge and told him to wait for his father. Then the hyenas started a stampede among a herd of wildebeest.

At that moment Mufasa was walking along a ridge with Zazu. "Simba!" he cried. "I'm coming!"

The King raced down the gorge and rescued his son, but he could not save himself.

He fell onto an overhanging rock as the wildebeest swept by him. Looking up he saw his brother.

"Scar, help me!" he cried. But Scar just leaned over and whispered, "Long live the King!" Then he pushed Mufasa into the path of the trampling wildebeest.

When the stampede was over, Simba ran to his father's side.

"Father," he whimpered, nuzzling Mufasa's mane. But the King did not reply, and Simba started sobbing.

"Simba," said Scar coldly, "what have you done? This is all your fault," he lied. "The King is dead and you must never show your face in the pride again. Run away and never return."

As Scar returned to take the royal throne at Pride Rock for himself, Simba stumbled exhausted and frightened through the grasslands towards the jungle. He took a few more shaky steps and collapsed. Hungry vultures circled above him.

Eventually Simba opened his eyes. A warthog, called Pumbaa, and Timon, a meerkat, were gazing down at him. They poured water into his dry mouth.

"You nearly died," said Pumbaa. "We saved you."

"Thanks for your help," said Simba, "but it doesn't matter. I've nowhere to go."

"Why not stay with us?" said Timon, kindly. "Put your past behind you. Remember! Hakuna matata – no worries! That's the way we live."

Simba thought for a moment and decided to stay in the jungle with his new friends.

Many years later, deep in a cave, Rafiki stared at a picture of a lion. "It is time," he said, smiling, and prepared to leave.

The very next day Simba rescued Pumbaa from a hungry lioness – it was Nala! The two friends were delighted to see each other again. Nala told Simba about Scar's reign of terror at Pride Rock and begged him to return. "With you alive, Scar has no right to the throne," she said.

"I can't go back. I'm not fit to be a king," Simba said sadly.

"You could be," Nala told him.

Simba showed Nala his favourite places in the jungle. "It's beautiful," she said. "I can see why you like it – but it's not your home. You're hiding from the future." She turned and left her friend alone.

That night Simba lay by a stream thinking. He heard a noise and looked up.

"Come with me," said Rafiki.

"I will take you to your father."

Simba followed him in wonder to the edge of the stream. As Simba looked into the water, his reflection gradually changed shape and became his father's!

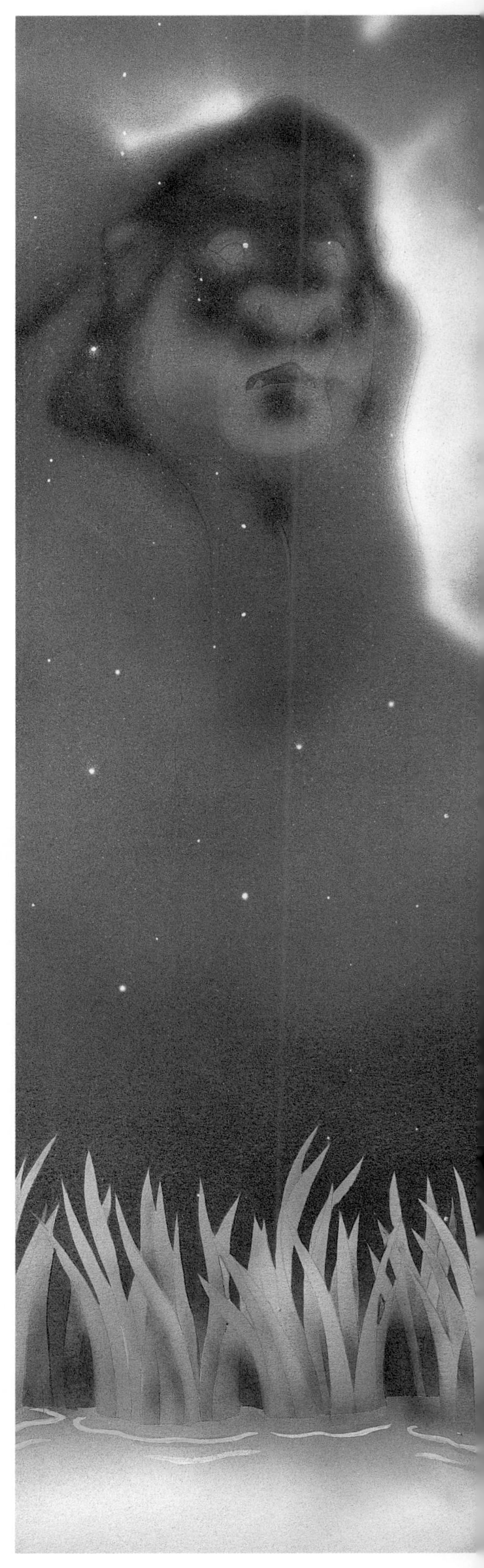

The reflection rose into the sky and Simba heard Mufasa's voice:

"Simba. You must take your place in the Circle of Life. You are my son and the one true King." Then the reflection and Rafiki disappeared.

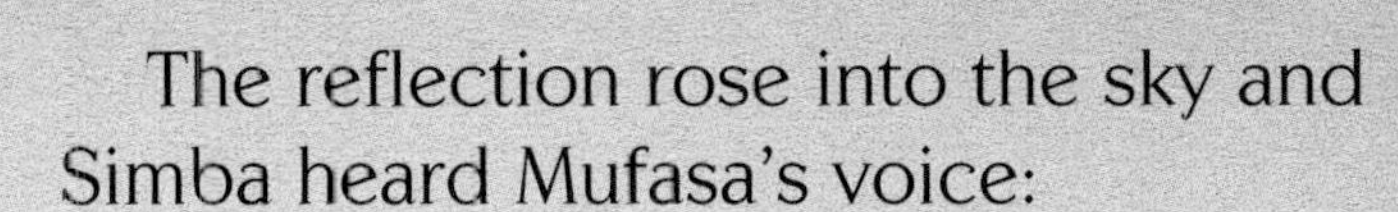

Back at Pride Rock, the rains had been late coming and the land was dry. The hyenas paced impatiently round King Scar.

"We're starving," they howled. "The herds have gone. There's nothing left to eat."

Storm clouds gathered in the sky and a lightning bolt scorched the earth. As the dry grasses caught fire, flames swept towards Pride Rock. A lion appeared through the smoke. It was Simba!

Scar lunged at Simba, determined to kill him just as he had Mufasa. In the fierce battle that followed, Simba finally heaved Scar over the cliff face. Scar called to the hyenas to save him, but Nala and the lionesses drove them back. Simba was victorious!

Nala went to Simba's side. "Welcome home!" she whispered.

As they smiled at each other, it started to rain. The heavy drops soaked the dry ground and streambeds filled up once more. The plains came back to life and the herds returned.

One dawn the animals and birds made their way again to the foot of Pride Rock. Watched by the lions, Pumbaa and Timon, Rafiki picked up a tiny cub. He showed the new Prince – the son of King Simba and Queen Nala – to the cheering crowd below.

That night Simba watched the stars rise in the sky. "Everything's all right, Father," he said softly. "You see, I remembered." And the stars seemed to twinkle in reply.

THE END

Snow White and the Seven Dwarfs

SNOW WHITE

THE PRINCE

STARRING

THE QUEEN

THE SEVEN DWARFS

Disney
Snow White
and the Seven Dwarfs

Once upon a time, there lived a princess called Snow White. Snow White's father was dead, so she lived with her wicked stepmother, the Queen.

Snow White was very beautiful. Her skin was as white as snow, her hair as black as ebony wood, and her lips were as red as a red, red rose.

The Queen was also very beautiful but very vain. She had a magic mirror and every day she would look into it and say:

"Magic mirror on the wall,
Who is the fairest one of all?"

The mirror would always reply:
"You, O Queen, are the
fairest of them all."

But the Queen was still jealous of Snow White and made her work in the castle as a servant.

One day, after the Queen had spoken to her magic mirror, the mirror replied:

"Famed is thy beauty, Majesty,
But behold, a lovely maid I see.
Alas, she is more fair than thee,
Lips as red as a rose,
Hair as black as ebony,
Skin as white as snow."

The Queen was furious. "Snow White!" she hissed. "It cannot be!"

At that very moment, Snow White was singing beside the castle well.

A handsome prince, who was passing by, stopped to listen. As soon as the Prince and Snow White saw each other, they fell in love.

When the Queen saw Snow White with the Prince, she was furious and decided to get rid of her stepdaughter.

The next morning, the Queen told her huntsman to take Snow White into the forest and kill her. "Bring back her heart to prove she is dead," she ordered.

The Huntsman led the Princess into the forest but he could not kill her. He told Snow White to hide in the forest. Then he took an animal's heart to show the Queen that the Princess was dead.

Snow White wandered deep into the forest. She was very scared but the animals led her to a little cottage. Snow White knocked on the door and went inside. She wondered who could live in such a tiny house.

There were seven dusty little chairs at the table. In the sink there were seven dirty spoons and bowls. And in the bedroom there were seven unmade tiny beds.

"Perhaps untidy children live here," Snow White said.

So, with the help of her forest friends, Snow White dusted and cleaned the little cottage. Then she lay across three of the tiny beds and fell asleep.

Evening came and the owners of the cottage returned.

They were Seven Dwarfs, who worked in diamond mines, deep in the heart of the mountain. The Dwarfs marched along singing:

"Heigh-ho, heigh-ho,
It's home from work we go!"

As soon as they entered the cottage, they knew something was wrong – it was clean! The floor had been swept and there was a delicious smell coming from a pot on the fire.

"What's happened?" they asked each other in amazement.

They searched the cottage for an intruder. They reached the bedroom just as Snow White was waking up.

"Who are you?" they asked.

"My name is Snow White," said Snow White. She explained what she was doing there. Then she asked the little men who they were.

One by one, the Dwarfs introduced themselves.
"I'm Doc."
"I'm Grumpy."
"I'm Bashful."
"I'm Sleepy."
"I'm Sneezy."
"I'm Happy."
"And he's Dopey," they all shouted together.

"I'm very pleased to meet you all," said Snow White. "If you let me stay here, I promise I'll look after the house for you. I'll wash and sew and cook."

The Dwarfs quickly agreed!

That evening, the cottage was filled with music and laughter. The Dwarfs sang and danced to welcome the Princess to their home. Snow White was so happy that she soon forgot all about her wicked stepmother.

Meanwhile, back in the castle, the wicked stepmother said the special words to the magic mirror, and the mirror replied:

"Snow White, who dwells with the Seven Dwarfs,
Is as fair as you and as fair again."

The Queen was furious. "Snow White must still be alive!" she screamed. She vowed to get rid of Snow White once and for all.

Down in the dungeon, the Queen cast a magic spell to disguise herself as an old pedlar woman. Then, chanting a magic spell, she dipped a bright red apple into a pot of bubbling poison.

"One bite of this and Snow White will fall into a sleep as if dead," she cackled. "Only a kiss from her true love will wake her!"

The very next day, after the Dwarfs had left for work, the old pedlar woman called on Snow White selling apples.

"Try one, pretty maid," said the pedlar, handing Snow White an apple. "One bite and all your dreams will come true."

Snow White took one bite and fell to the floor as if dead.

"Now I'm the fairest in the land!" cried the wicked Queen, before fleeing.

Luckily, Snow White's forest friends had seen what had happened and went to fetch the Seven Dwarfs.

As the Dwarfs rushed towards the cottage, they spotted the Queen running away. They chased her through the forest and up the mountain.

The wicked Queen tried to roll a huge boulder on the dwarfs. But it rolled back and pushed her over the side of the mountain – never to be seen again.

When the Dwarfs returned to the cottage, they found Snow White lying on the floor as if she were dead. They could not wake her, so they took her into the forest. They placed her on a special bed and kept watch over her every day.

The months slowly passed. Snow White's bed was covered with leaves, then snow, and then the blossoms of spring.

She still did not wake up.

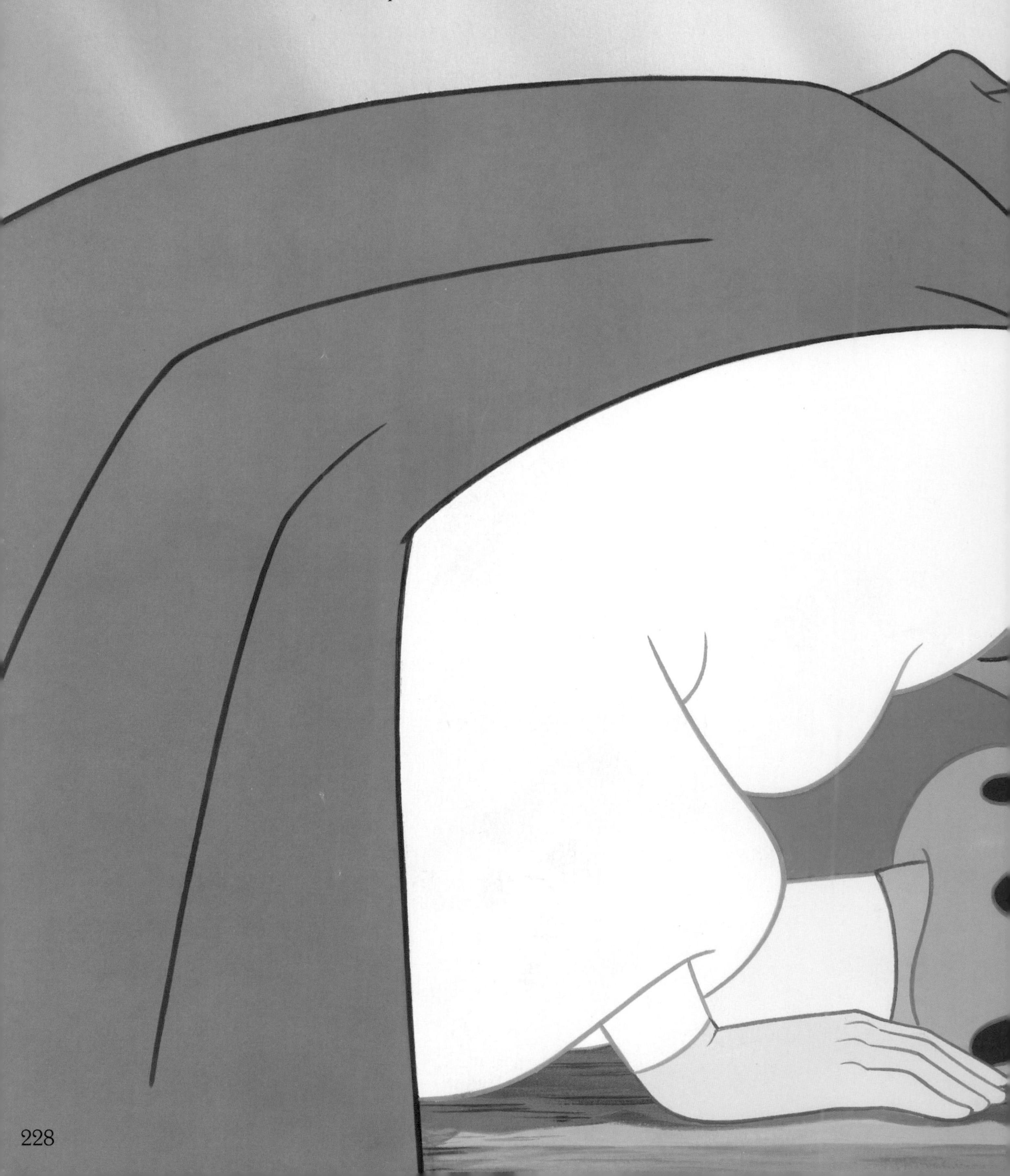

One day, a handsome young man came riding through the forest. He was the Prince who had fallen in love with Snow White by the castle well. When he saw the Princess, he got down from his horse, leant over her and kissed her.

All at once, Snow White's eyes fluttered open.

"She's awake!" the Dwarfs cried, excitedly. The wicked Queen's spell was broken.

Before Snow White left to begin her new life with the Prince, she kissed each of the Dwarfs. "I'll come and see you very soon," she promised them.

The Dwarfs watched the Prince lead Snow White away to her new life. They knew they would miss her but they also knew that she and the Prince would live happily ever after.

THE END

SPACE RANGER
LIGHTYEAR
LASER

WALL·E